THE BLIZZARD

The snowstorm that buried Dorset

MARK CHING

Published by Mark Ching

THE BLIZZARD OF 78
The snowstorm that buried Dorset

First printing September 2008
Second printing December 2008

ISBN 978-0-9560553-0-9

First published 2008 by
Mark Ching
Langmor
High Street
Winfrith Newburgh
Dorset DT2 8JW

Printed in Great Britain for Mark Ching

THE BLIZZARD OF 78

The snowstorm that buried Dorset

Front cover photo:
Massive snowdrifts tower over John Hodgson on the Ridgeway
as he walks from Weymouth to Dorchester on Monday 20th
February 1978 © John Hodgson.

This book is dedicated to all those who have a fascination with our ever changing weather.

CONTENTS

Acknowledgements

The Blizzard of 78 has taken a year to put together and has taken the great majority of my spare time and so my first thank you must go to my long suffering wife Julie for uncomplainingly giving me the time and space to concentrate on the project. Thanks Jools.

The book itself would not have come together without the help of a great many people.

I would like to thank

The Royal Meteorological society for permission to reproduce the relevant weather maps that appeared in the weather log section that accompanied the April 1978 edition (Volume 33 Issue 4) of Weather Magasine.

Dr Richard Wild at WeatherNet Ltd for permission to use information from: Wild, R. (2005) *A spatial and temporal analysis of heavy snowfalls across Great Britain between the years 1861-1999*. Unpublished PhD Thesis, University of Derby, 344 pp.

Helen Crosbie for her invaluable help with proof reading.

Special thanks to former Assistant Chief Constable of Dorset Len Burt for his assistance regarding the emergency situation on the ground at the time of the blizzard.

Neal Butterworth. Editor. Scott Harrison and Nick Churchill at the Bournemouth Daily Echo.

David Murdock, Editor. Ruth Meech, Arts editor at the Dorset Echo.

Tim Dixon, Editor. Western Gazette.

John Newth, Editor. Dorset Life Magasine.

Bournemouth News and Picture agency.

I am hugely indebted to the following people who supplied their stories or photographs and in many cases both.

Ken Ayres. Richard Baker. Mrs B. Barter. Mr R Beggs. Graham Bendell. Mr P Brewin. Alan Brown. Nigel Bryant. Brian Bugler. Margaret Byrne. Ronald Ching. Margaret Crowther. Pete Dear. John Dunk. Julie Dyball. Michael Edwards. Julia Goodwin. Noreen Guy. Jo, John and Bernard Hammick. Colin Haysom. Ray Hazell. Mrs Hobby. John Hodgson. Patricia Hoff. Derek Huxley. Joyce Ingham. Arthur and Irene Jeanes. Julie Kent. Peter Kerslake. Prim Lee. Diane Liddell. Felicity Maclaren. Maureen Marchant. Neil Matthews. John 'Kiwi' Mays. Pat Middle. Paul Miller. Jo Mullen. Peter Nevill. Brendon Owen. Di Phillips. Josie Pleavin. Chris and Lyn Pullen. Brian Searle. Maureen Smith. Ruth Smith. Colonel. D. Squirell. Mr L. Stainer. Anne and Alan Stephens. Andrew Symmons. Jenny Vincent. Peter Walker. Richard and Sheila Weller. Norman Wellstead. Mrs D. Wheeler. Vicki Wright.

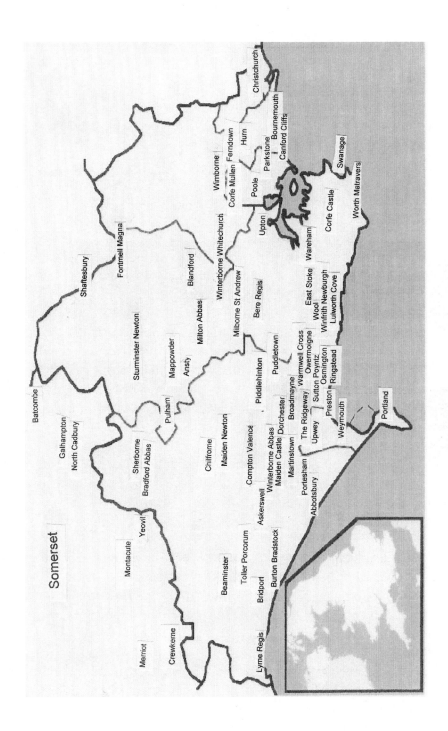

Somerset

Merriot
Montacute
Crewkerne
Yeovil
Batcombe
Galhampton
North Cadbury
Sherborne
Bradford Abbas
Lyme Regis
Burton Bradstock
Bridport
Toller Porcorum
Beaminster
Askerswell
Pulham
Chilfrome
Maiden Newton
Compton Valence
Winterborne Abbas
Maiden Castle
Dorchester
Martinstown
Portesham
Abbotsbury
Upwey
The Ridgeway
Broadmayne
Sutton Poyntz
Preston
Ringstead
Weymouth
Portland
Mappowder
Ansty
Milton Abbas
Sturminster Newton
Piddletrenthide
Piddlehinton
Puddletown
Warmwell Cross
Owermoigne
Osmington
Shaftesbury
Fontmell Magna
Blandford
Winterborne Whitechurch
Milborne St Andrew
Bere Regis
East Stoke
Wool
Winfrith Newburgh
Lulworth Cove
Wareham
Corfe Castle
Worth Matravers
Swanage
Upton
Poole
Corfe Mullen
Wimborne
Ferndown
Hurn
Parkstone
Bournemouth
Canford Cliffs
Christchurch

9

Forward

Severe winter weather is not something that people associate with Dorset. The county is after all set in the most sheltered part of the most temperate mainland area of the British isles.

The recent warming trend in our climate coupled with the lack of land above a thousand feet seems to have pushed Dorset to the very margins in terms of snowfall and away from the hilly ground in the north, snow has become an increasingly infrequent visitor, rarely, if ever, settling on the ground for more than a few hours or so. It has not been unusual for coastal locations in the south and southwest to see no lying snow at all in a winter in recent times. Indeed it has almost become the norm.

Whatever your opinion of snow, whether you love it or loathe it, I would venture to suggest that this continuing lack of noteworthy snowfall is a sad thing. Writing this as I enter my forty eighth year, I and those of a similar age have at least in our own childhoods had the chance enjoy the immense fun that a deep snowfall can bring; whether it be sledging, snowballing, building a snowman or even an igloo.

Spare a thought then for the generation of youngsters across the county who have never had the chance for such fun, having had to make do with the pitiful smatterings that have tried to pass themselves off as snowfall in recent years.

When you tell them that you can remember a time not so very long ago when it snowed so hard that people were marooned in their villages or towns for days on end, or that the snowdrifts were so deep that you could stand on them and touch the tops of telegraph poles, they look at you as if you have come from another planet.

Older folk can of course hark back to the winters of legend. The bitter cold and snow of 1963 or the endless blizzards and post war deprivations of 1947. My own great grandmother could do even better by recalling from her childhood days in Sherborne, the immense Victorian snowstorms of January 1881 and March 1891, when level snow was some twenty four inches deep with drifts as high as thirty feet or more! Both events saw her having to climb out of her first floor bedroom window because all the downstairs doors and windows were buried underneath the snow! Much of my own childhood was spent hoping that the ghosts of those great Victorian winters would rattle their chains once more.

Three memorable things happened to me in the first two months of 1978. Firstly my family moved from the suburbs of Bournemouth to the village of Worth Matravers in the Purbeck Hills. Secondly I turned Eighteen in early February and thirdly the most severe individual weather event of my life took place on the weekend of 18th/19th February. It was an interesting few weeks to say the least.

The winter of 1977/8 had not been desperately cold. Indeed it is not even in the top twenty coldest winters of the twentieth century; However the cold spell between the 8th and 20th February 1978 was as fierce as anything from 1947 or 1963 and as an individual event the blizzard of the 18/19th February was deeper and more intense in Dorset than the snowstorms from either of those long lasting winters.

In the following pages you will find the story of a very rare event indeed; The story of the greatest individual snowstorm to hit Dorset in the last one hundred years.

This is the story of "The Blizzard of 78"

The Beast from the east awakes

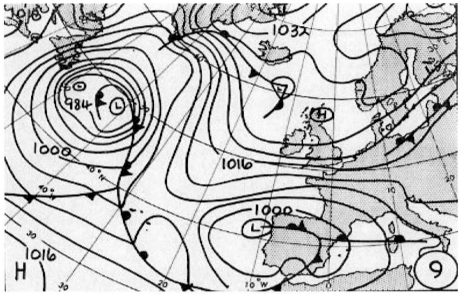

© Crown Copyright - provided by the Met Office.

The 'Beast from the east awakes! 1200hrs 9th February 1978. The pressure map above shows a vast area of high pressure to the north and east of the UK. Air flows clockwise around an area of high pressure indicating that the bitterly cold air flowing across southern England actually originated somewhere over north west Russia.

The winters of the early to mid 1970's had on the whole been mild and relatively snow free in Dorset especially on low ground This was a distinct change from the 1960's when at least one substantial snowfall had occurred even on the low ground in seven out of the ten winters .

During early January 1978 the usual procession of Atlantic low pressure systems was keeping the UK in a mild south-westerly flow for much of the time. However, around mid month a subtle change occurred as the low pressure systems started to dive south-eastwards across the UK and head into central Europe; A change that resulted in some snow for the northern half of the UK and a colder feel to the damp weather in the south.

This subtle change was brought about by a substantial rise in pressure to the north and north-east of the UK creating what meteorologists call a blocking high (and what cold weather lovers refer to as the "Beast from the East") forcing the low pressure areas to take a more southerly track than usual. During the first few days of February the blocking high really began to exert its influence, not only diverting the low pressure systems, but, by the end of the first week, holding them at bay out in the Atlantic Ocean. Meanwhile because the circulation of air around an area of a high pressure is clockwise, bitterly cold easterly winds were heading out of northern Europe and Scandinavia and across the North Sea towards the UK.

The "Beast from the East" had awakened and was about to make its presence felt in no uncertain terms.

In the early hours the of the 9th February, the temperature plummeted to minus 5°C and showers gave a light covering of snow across Dorset. During the 9th, the temperature across the county struggled to climb above freezing point and overnight into the 10th, the mercury plummeted down to minus 6°C in urban areas and much lower than this at rural locations. Dorset was not alone however and counties across England and Wales were feeling the effects of the icy easterly blast with two hundred thousand miles of roads affected by ice or snow.

Early on the morning of Saturday 11th, Bournemouth (minus 6.9°C) recorded its lowest temperature for five years and Poole (minus 6.3°C) its lowest for nine years while at Hurn airport the mercury had plummeted to minus 7.7°C. The cold was showing no sign of abating and further a field even that mildest of locations the Scilly Isles were reporting their first snow since the Siberian winter of 1963!

A measure of the sheer intensity of the cold gripping the south can be gained from the experience of firefighters attending a blaze in a bungalow at Merley near Wimborne. They found that water from their hoses was freezing instantly on the ground creating ice rink conditions just a few yards from the blazing building. Council workers had to be called out to apply grit.

Clear night skies during the weekend of 11th and 12th of February allowed temperatures to drop even further, inducing the coldest weekend in east Dorset since 1956. In Bournemouth a bone numbing minus 11.5°C was recorded whilst Poole plunged almost as low with minus 10.4°C. Little wonder then that local newspaper reports at the start of the new working week on Monday 13th were excitedly telling of the many lakes and ponds that had frozen solid right across the county. These included the lakes at Poole park and the harbour at West Bay. In Weymouth the upper harbour was starting to freeze, as was Radipole lake.

Elsewhere in Weymouth at Lodmoor, the frozen lakes and ponds gave fourteen year old Alison Roberts, her sister Michelle and their friends Susan and Stephen Hughes a Monday they wouldn't forget in a hurry.

The four youngsters were walking a collie dog called Lucy belonging to Mrs Sybill Cassidy. The dog had made its way out onto an ice covered pond but fell through into the water. Alison made her way across the ice to try and rescue the dog but went through as well. Her friend Susan tried to rescue her and she in turn went through the ice as did both Michelle and Stephen leaving them all waist deep in freezing water. Three of the youngsters managed to get out but Alison was stuck because her boots had been sucked into the mud. Stephen Hughes then threw Alison his scarf in order to pull her out. A passer by called the fire brigade and using a ladder laid upon the ice they managed to rescue Lucy the collie, leaving a happy if very chilly ending to the story.

Sadly in other parts of the UK the "big freeze" as the press were now calling it, had taken a deadly toll with two young boys falling through the ice on ponds and drowning in northern England. Elsewhere, the harsh winter conditions over the weekend had claimed the lives of four climbers in Scotland and Snowdonia.

By midweek however better news was on the way, or so it seemed. A thaw was on the way trumpeted the Bournemouth Evening Echo in its edition on the Wednesday 15th February. Quoting the Met Office. "Some sleet with snow possible on higher ground quickly turning to rain during the night ushering in milder weather."

However, things didn't go according to plan.

"The worst since 63"

During the evening of the Wednesday 15th, the forecast sleet duly arrived, but that is where any similarity between the actual weather and the Met Office forecast ended. Instead of turning to rain the sleet quickly turned to heavy snow even on low ground.

The low pressure system that was predicted to bring the milder weather was not playing ball. Instead of sweeping across southern England bringing milder air and a thaw in its wake, it slipped south-eastwards across the west country keeping Dorset in the bitterly cold air but feeding in a mass of moisture which fell as snow.

Heavy snow started to fall early in the evening and quickly started to cause havoc on roads in the west and north of the county. Conditions deteriorated very quickly. The A37 northwards from Dorchester to Yeovil quickly became impassable as did the A35 westwards from Dorchester to Bridport and the coast road via Abbotsbury. Two coach loads of music lovers from the Bridport area who were on their way to a concert by the Bournemouth Sinfonietta were forced to turn back due to the conditions.

At Portland, a meeting of the council planning committee convened to discuss a report on the island's stone industry had just got underway with deputy county council planning officer Kenneth Cross outlining the report and its proposals when news reached the chamber of the conditions outside. Councillors Elsie Wright and Nora Brown who had arrived late plastered in snow described conditions on the hill as becoming impassable. Council members were given the choice to leave if they wished to do so. Town mayor Fred Morris along with councillors Wright and Brown decided to try and get home whilst they still could. As this left a minority of the committee to discuss a very important issue, the meeting was postponed until a later date.

Meanwhile at the Lee household in Court Orchard Road in Bridport, an eventful evening just was beginning to unfold. Mrs Angela Lee was expecting her second child and duly went into labour at about half past seven. Two hours later an ambulance manned by Jim Williams and Roger Hansford arrived to take Mrs Lee on the half hour journey to Dorchester but with road conditions by now extremely difficult the journey would in the end take some two and a half hours. After travelling about five miles towards Dorchester, the ambulance became stuck in the snow and the crew were left waiting for a police land rover to arrive and tow them the rest of the way.

The land rover duly arrived but almost straight away had to tow the ambulance into a lay-by near the Travellers rest because Mrs Lee's baby had decided it was time to greet the world. As is always the case with our emergency workers they remained calm and reassuring throughout what they described later as a quite normal delivery. Mrs Lee gave birth to a baby boy and described the crew as really wonderful.

Conditions deteriorated even further on that stretch of road and by late evening some twenty people had taken refuge at the Askers Roadhouse. As late as half past two the next morning a family of seven, who were travelling to Plymouth from Portsmouth, turned up there having had to abandon their vehicle. All minor roads on high ground were also impassable and overnight, snowdrifts several feet deep continued to build up.

By the early hours it had become clear that the snowplough crews would have to be called out. They swung into action on the A35 and the A37 at three o'clock and within an hour had made it through to Dorchester on both of these roads. Crews were also busy at work on the roads connecting Blandford with Sturminster Newton and Shaftesbury. In the west another crew had got through from Bridport to Misterton Cross. The main problem on the higher routes was that although the ploughs made it through, the strong winds were blowing fallen snow back across the roads and the ploughs had to remain in action to try and keep the roads clear for emergency traffic. As usual the crews had to deal with the problem of abandoned vehicles. Around Blandford some four inches of snow had fallen in an hour during the evening leaving the vehicle owners with little alternative but to get out and walk!

It was also during the early hours that Gilbert Curtis, Weymouth's award winning baker, had set off to go to a trade show in Swansea. With three colleagues, and a boot full of his award winning produce they had set off at four in the morning. After sliding most of the way up the A37 between Dorchester and the Clay Pigeon, they ground to a halt in a huge snowdrift around five o'clock and remained there until a snow plough caught up with them some four hours later.

On the lower ground in the east of the county most roads around Bournemouth were still passable with care although emergency services had a busy night dealing with accidents. Police had in fact closed the southbound carriageway of the A338 spur road into Bournemouth from ten o'clock in the evening until half past seven the following morning as the road had become a "skating rink".

Across the county boundary in Hampshire, roads across the New Forest had been gritted and salted throughout the night, although this didn't particularly help in the case of a Hampshire county council highways superintendent whose van left the A31 between Cadnam and Picket Post whist he was checking out road conditions overnight. Shaken but unhurt the superintendent managed to climb out of the vehicle report back to his employers and was back at his post for work in the morning.

Meanwhile back in Dorset, Divisional Surveyor Brian Doyle reporting on conditions around Dorchester and the west continued to make the point about the battle that the ploughs were having trying to clear the main roads, which essentially were only to be used by emergency services. Minor roads in many parts were still impassable despite sterling work by farmers with snowploughs fitted on their tractors. They were finding the same problem as the other clearance crews namely the wind blowing the snow back across the roads as quickly as they were clearing them. The main call was for people not to make unnecessary journeys and get stuck hindering the work of the crews. Mr Doyle put it quite bluntly. "I have scant time for private motorists who make unnecessary journeys." He said; This was echoed by the police who described conditions on the morning of the 16th as "treacherous".

The overnight snow had also caused problems with power supplies in some parts of the county with the lights going out around Puncknowle, West Bexington, Little and Long Bredy and Maiden Newton in the west. Whilst Bovington and Worth Matravers had been blacked out further east. Southern Electricity Board workmen had worked through the night often finding that their land rovers were getting stuck in snowdrifts up to four feet deep before they even managed to get to the power lines in question.

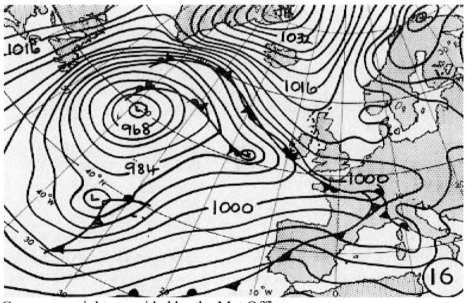

Crown copyright- provided by the Met Office

The pressure map above shows the situation at midday on the 16th Feb with the low pressure area that brought the snow on the night of the 15th now over central Europe and a new low pressure area forming just to the west of Ireland and ready to dive south eastwards across the west country bringing more snow to Dorset on the night of the 16th.

As the Dorset skies cleared a little during the 16th and dusk approached, most Dorset folk were probably wondering what conditions would be like the following morning once the inevitable severe overnight frost had frozen all the snow and slush that had not melted during the day. As things turned out frost was not going to be the main concern. By late after noon another low pressure system was waiting out west with its attendant moisture but yet again the cold air proved too strong and the system slipped south eastwards across the west country, throwing moisture into the cold air over Dorset. By mid evening another blizzard was blowing across the county.

Once again it was the west of the county that took the brunt. By ten o'clock that evening the snowploughs trying to keep the A35 clear reported that they were fighting a losing battle and were withdrawn until conditions improved later in the night. The A35 west of Dorchester was reopened at seven in the morning after yet more sterling work by the snowplough crews. The A37 between Dorchester and Yeovil took another severe hit from the overnight snow but yet again the snow plough crews managed to make some headway and the road was declared "open but very difficult and needing great care." The A352 Dorchester to Sherborne Road was put in the same "passable with care" category but the old Sherborne road was completely blocked at Giants Head and the coast road between Weymouth and Bridport was blocked at Abbotsbury hill.

East of Dorchester, there were severe problems on Yellowham hill near Puddletown where up to ten vehicles including an articulated lorry had become stuck and were blocking the road. Back in 1978 the A35 between Bere Regis and Dorchester was a single carriageway road and not the wide open quasi motorway that it is now. Major delays ensued on this main east-west transport route with long delays at Bere Regis backing up all the way to the Bakers arms roundabout between Poole and Wareham. In general though, many drivers had learnt the lesson of the previous night and booked themselves into pubs and hotels once the conditions worsened leaving far fewer abandoned vehicles to impede the snow clearing crews.

However, even taking shelter had its perils as one traveller at the Askers Motel found when he had to be dug out of his chalet because a four foot snowdrift blocked the door!

Conditions in the east of the county were not quite as bad as further west illustrated by the fact that at Hurn airport the weather station reported some two inches of snow whilst at Dorchester Football club some six inches of snow covered the pitch. An even more glaring and very local disparity was that between Dorchester and Weymouth town centre where there was no lying snow at all. Drivers travelling towards Weymouth left the snowy conditions behind at Radipole. Weymouth however was the exception.

Across the great majority of the county minor roads in particular were blocked or at best passable only with extreme care. It was in this regard that Dorset's farmers came into their own. Under an agreement with the county council, farmers were given snowploughs which can fit onto tractors. These were stored away until such time as they were needed, when they would be fitted and used to clear minor roads in rural areas. They proved an immense help, with farmers working tirelessly to help clear away at least some of the previous two nights snowfall.

Even today one can still spot some of these snowploughs stored in lay-bys at the side of the road. Many have remained unused throughout recent winters but they're still there, ready for when the next 'big one' comes.

After two successive nights with substantial snowfall a little light relief came in the way of a few hours of weak winter sunshine as Friday 17th wore on. This was more than enough to tempt some Dorset residents to get outside and start some snow clearing around their properties. Sadly this led to a tragic event at Broadwindsor where the Reverend R.W.G. Vincent fell ill shortly after clearing snow at the vicarage. He died shortly afterwards. He was just forty nine years old and the father of five sons; A reminder if one were needed that even in our generally temperate climate weather events can have a very high human cost. Reverend Vincent was not the only one. The severe cold of the previous two weeks had seen a substantial increase in the number of elderly people being found dead in or near to their homes.

Meanwhile at Canford School near Wimborne a young student named Bernard Hammick was feeling distinctly unwell, so much so that the school rang his parents and asked them to collect him and take him home. Little did he know it but by the time the weekend was over young Bernard would be making the front pages of the national press.

The cold spell had now been bringing freezing weather to the county for over two weeks and was now without doubt the most potent spell of winter weather since the legendary winter of 1963 some fifteen years earlier. Surely now some respite would come?

The few sunny hours during Friday did indeed prove to be a relief however it would be but a fleeting respite. Saturday 18th dawned grey and dank with a bitter east wind.

To the north east of the UK the high pressure was holding firm feeding sub zero air across southern England. Meanwhile in the south west approaches yet another low pressure system and its weather front laden with moisture was heading for southern England. The scene was being set for yet another snowy encounter but this time it wouldn't be just a few hours of snowfall. This time the titanic struggle between the opposing air masses would create a snowstorm lasting up to thirty hours in some places, driven on by severe gale force winds. The worst blizzard for nearly a hundred years was set to bury the county.

The Blizzard of 78 was about to strike.

The Blizzard strikes.

Saturday afternoon and evening

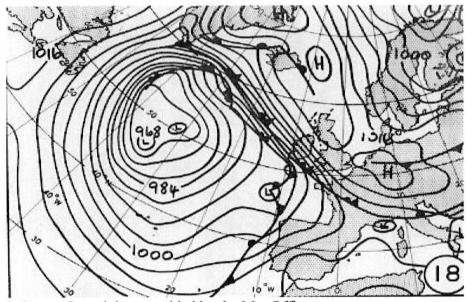

© Crown Copyright - provided by the Met Office

The pressure map shown above displays the situation at 1200 GMT. The high pressure which has been anchored to the north and east of the UK for the past ten days is feeding bitterly cold air from the arctic and eastern Europe across Britain whilst moisture laden weather fronts battle to make headway into the south west England.

Saturday 18th February was a bitterly cold day made all the more miserable by grey leaden skies. The temperature hovered a degree or two above freezing but the rising easterly wind made it feel far colder. The wind chill equivalent of 2°C in a twenty miles per hour wind is around minus 10°C.

The author's own experience of that day in Wareham and Swanage bears this out.

" I was already two years into a thatching apprenticeship so I was used to being outdoors in all weathers and dressed for it accordingly but this was something different! I can remember getting out of the car in Wareham and the cold cut through me like a knife. It was a truly bitter day."

"We visited Mr Curtis the butcher and it was a huge relief just to get inside his shop. It was in that shop that we got our first inkling of the severity of the blizzard that was to come our way later in the day. Mr Curtis told us that he had listened to the early morning farming programme on Radio Four and that the forecast had warned farmers, particularly those in the south west of the serious nature of the weather that was expected to hit during the evening."

"From Wareham, we moved on to Swanage and lunch at the Mowlem Restaurant on the sea front. We parked by the old railway station and walked the couple of hundred yards up Station Road towards the sea front. It felt like a couple of hundred miles walking into the teeth of a wind that seemed to have blown directly into Swanage from somewhere in Siberia! Welcome refuge was found once more in the Mowlem restaurant itself. However, with a strong east wind blasting across the bay, the sea was a tad on the wild side and lunch was accompanied by the somewhat unnerving experience of waves breaking against the base of the building and splattering spray across the restaurant windows a couple of floors above."

"When we made our way back to the car, the streets of Swanage were practically deserted. It's hardly surprising really, even some 30 years later that Saturday with its miserable combination of leaden skies and bitter winds sticks in my mind as perhaps the bleakest winters day I can remember."

"It's not just me either. Over the last ten years I have given talks about Dorset weather all over the county and whenever the conversation gets round to 1978, the rawness of that bleak Saturday before the blizzard struck is always mentioned."

The wicked east wind that rose throughout the day was the result of the increasing struggle for supremacy between the High pressure to the north east pulling the bitter air in from the east and the low pressure at the mouth of the English channel in the south western approaches.

The first signs of the impending blizzard came with sleet and snow arriving in the tip of Cornwall at around six o'clock on that Saturday morning. It is a sign of the titanic struggle between the two air masses that it would be another twelve hours before blizzard conditions would be knocking on the door of East Dorset. In normal 'unopposed' conditions, a similar weather system might have taken two or three hours to cover the same ground.

By noon the advancing blizzard had reached a line roughly from Barnstaple to Plymouth with observers living on the upper reaches of Dartmoor describing a wall of white advancing across the moor and then engulfing them and covering the ground within minutes!

By now travellers who were already in the blizzard were having to abandon their vehicles and seek sanctuary wherever they could and by mid afternoon all snowploughs, gritting vehicles and AA patrols had to be called off the higher ground for fear of becoming trapped themselves. Conditions on the moors of the southwest were incredibly severe with screaming winds not only whipping the snow into drifts but uprooting trees as well. At Lydford, the famous Lydford Gorge suffered immense damage with hundreds of trees blown over and in one particular instance a hundred hectare forest of thirty year old fir trees was flattened by funnelling winds thought to be excess of one hundred miles per hour!

Meanwhile at the top of Overcombe Drive in Weymouth and despite the bitter wind Brian Searle was turning over his vegetable patch in readiness for planting his broad beans. With an old transistor radio for company he listened with interest as a sports report from Plymouth told of a football league match being abandoned due to falling snow. He thought to himself if heavy snow was falling down that way it was just possible that "we might be in for some flurries too".

With the blizzard raging its way across Devon, it was only a matter of time before Dorset was hit, and sure enough by mid afternoon the western half of the county was in its grip.

It was in the early afternoon that another Weymouth resident, Peter Walker left home to drive to work for his double shift at U.K.A.E.E. Winfrith, where he worked on the atomic reactor. The ongoing severe cold weather meant that the reactor had to generate one hundred megawatts of power into the national grid continuously, twenty four hours a day. A few flakes were fluttering about as Peter drove to work, and by about three o'clock it had started to snow in earnest. By the time darkness fell at about five o'clock drifts were starting to form against the tall chain link boundary fence. Peter got the feeling he would not be driving home at the end of his shift and moved his car so it was sheltered by the cycle shed. What Peter didn't know on that Saturday tea-time was just how long his 'double shift' would turn out to be!

Meanwhile at Bridport Road in Dorchester Richard Baker had waved off his wife and two young children as they went off to the Plaza cinema to see, somewhat appropriately, "Snow white and the seven dwarfs". He drew the curtains on the bleak and increasingly gloomy day outside and settled down to watch the rugby international between Wales and Scotland on television; The sunny conditions then prevailing in Cardiff giving Richard even less hint of what was happening outside behind his closed curtains. As the match wore on deep into the second half Richard noticed that Bridport Road had become very quiet but the match kept him engrossed. At the final whistle he drew back the curtains to stare incredulously at the sight that met his eyes.

As Richard himself puts it,

" No wonder it was quiet and there was no traffic noise; the road was completely blocked by snow. At this point I realised that my wife and children would have no idea what had happened because they were in the cinema. As I prepared to go and meet them three 'snowmen' appeared at the gate! Despite being a lifelong snow enthusiast the conditions were too severe to venture outside so we watched through the windows until midnight when the snow was level with our window sills!"

While Richard Baker had been watching the rugby, Weymouth college student Neil Matthews, and a couple of friends had spent the afternoon up on Maiden Castle. They were well dressed for the weather because their study of environmental science meant a good deal of their work was done outside. Even so they felt bitterly cold. Neil and his friends noticed that the sky was looking increasingly threatening and with the bitter wind rising even further decided to call it a day. Even before they got back to the car park snow was falling steadily and conditions were deteriorating with the grassy hillside starting to get covered.

Setting out along Maiden Castle road and then onto the A354 to Weymouth. Neil and his friends headed for home. They were hoping to see some views of Weymouth on the way back and decided to take the back road via Came Down and Coombe Valley. However shortly after turning off the main road it became apparent that no such views would be forthcoming. Weymouth was completely blotted out by the falling snow and behind them Dorchester had disappeared from view as well. By now the light was fading and the snow was settling fast on the little used minor roads.

They pressed on, down towards Coombe Valley were things became a bit tricky, with the road obscured by snow. Neil describes the view in his rear view mirror as looking "as if we were being pursued by an angry cloud of snow". He and his friends eventually made it down to the relatively busy Littlemoor Road where conditions were less severe and to this day he believes his was the last car to come down the 'back' road into Weymouth until after the thaw!

On the other side of the town Patricia Hoff and her family had travelled to

Bridport earlier in the day to buy one of the then "new fangled" Calor gas heaters that could be moved on wheels from room to room. By early afternoon it was time to head back towards Weymouth a journey given extra importance due to the fact that it was her daughters twelfth birthday that very day. However as they headed out onto the coast road the police were in the process of closing the route. Patricia was allowed through and would be the last car to travel that road until after the blizzard.

The suddenness of the onslaught and the speed with which conditions became difficult, particularly on the high ground was spectacular, and led to some remarkable battles for those caught out in the quickly deteriorating conditions.

In Dorchester Peter Nevill decided it was time to shut his shop in Great Western Road and head home to Abbotsbury. It would prove to be an immensely difficult journey and one that even now he feels he was somewhat lucky to survive.

Initially Peter drove out along the A35 to the Winterborne Steepleton turning on the outskirts of Winterborne Abbas and headed for Abbotsbury. He had travelled barely half a mile only to find the way blocked by a snowdrift. He returned to Dorchester hoping to find his way home via Weymouth and the Ridgeway, however there was queue of traffic because this road too was now blocked by snow. After considering his options which were by now very limited, he decided to return to Winterborne Steepleton, park his car and walk the four and half miles home to Abbotsbury from there; a not inconsiderable distance in good weather let alone a raging snowstorm.

Having asked a local farmer if he might leave his car in his yard he started out along Coombe Road in the direction Portesham on foot. The first couple of snowdrifts did not prove too much of a problem and Peter waded through the snow which had drifted to about two feet in depth. Encouraged by this he forged boldly on. However once he had cleared the wood that shelters the first part of the road things started to look very different indeed and Peter suddenly found himself waist deep in snow.

Without the shelter of the trees the gale driven snow felt like needles and now exposed to the full blast of the gale he could also feel the full effect of the severe cold. It should be remembered that Peter was wearing only his normal town clothes and no hat. Added to these handicaps it was now also very dark.

Climbing out of his waist-deep drift, Peter headed towards the bank at the side of the road and thought about walking across the fields but decided that it would be better stick to the fence line at the side of the road. Here at least the tops of the odd fence post could still be picked out as a guide to where the road was supposed to be.

After two hours of labouring through the white maelstrom he reached the cross roads to the west of Hardy's Monument where he came across a Mini almost completely buried in a snowdrift. Scraping the snow away, he was relieved to find that it was empty.

Turning right at the crossroads, Peter headed off on the final leg of his epic journey home along Bishops Road via Gorwell and White's Hill towards Abbotsbury. In places the severe gale had blown the road clear of snow making for some easier going in the early stages. However on reaching Whites hill, his feet went from under him and he slid a fair distance down the ice covered road before coming to a halt in a snowdrift. By now Peter was extremely cold and wet but from his snowdrift he could at last make out the lights of Abbotsbury and heartened by this, redoubled his efforts for the final push home.

Some thirty minutes later a battered and buffeted Peter Nevill stumbled through his own front door much to his wife's great relief. Looking somewhat aghast at her husband, Mrs Nevill couldn't help but notice that her husbands trousers were festooned below the knee with what appeared to be frozen pink pom-poms. The snow that had stuck to him on his slide down the hill had been stained with blood where he had ripped his legs on the barbed wire fence that he was following near the start, of his epic journey. Such were the numbing effects of the severe cold, Peter hadn't felt a thing. Peter was ill for several days as a result of his struggle with the elements but as he himself very succinctly puts it. " I was thankful that I was not dead under some snowdrift, where I probably wouldn't have been found until the thaw!"

Peter Nevill was not the only person to get caught out in that corner of Dorset. Just across the other side of the A35 Peter Kerslake and a colleague were working for Post Office Telephones (the precursor to BT) on a house at Compton Valence. By mid afternoon snow was beginning to fall quite quickly and after working a little longer Peter and his colleague decided to make a break for it while they still could because whichever way you go to leave Compton Valence you have to go uphill at some point and by now the snow was starting to settle on the roads.

They headed out of the village towards the old roman road that joins up with the A35 a mile or so east of Winterbourne Abbas. Conditions on the roman road on top of the hill however were far worse than they had been down in the village, the windscreen wipers on their van could not cope with the blinding snow and they had to keep getting out to clear the windscreen as they picked their way along the narrow road.

It was almost inevitable in the rapidly deteriorating conditions that they would run into a snowdrift. Which they duly did, coming to a halt in a wall of snow that was already higher than their little van.

It was decision time. With snow building up around the van very quickly, They had to do something or risk being buried alive under the snow. After a short discussion they decided that because they had keys to the telephone exchange at Maiden Newton, they should try and make their way there across country. Indeed, with the deep west Dorset lanes rapidly filling up with huge drifts going across the open fields was their only option.

They left the vehicle and set out back towards Compton Valence in what was by now a howling blizzard and within 20 minutes of getting out of the vehicle the snowdrifts had reached seven to eight feet in height. Keeping to the fields meant climbing over fences and through hedges but as long as they kept parallel to the road between Compton Valence and Maiden Newton they would heading in the right direction.

It was an immense battle just to stand up and try to see anything through the driving snow let alone make headway toward the safety of the exchange at Maiden Newton, but after battling the blizzard for three or four hours they made it to the Maiden Newton exchange and put a call into a colleague from Dorchester who braved the severe conditions on the A37 to drive out to Maiden Newton and pick them up. By the time they reached the outskirts of Dorchester they were coming past signs put out by the police announcing that the road they had just travelled was already closed. The van that they had left high up on the hill above Compton Valence would remain buried for four days!

The weather fronts that were creating the blizzard conditions as they ran into the cold air were slowly making their way across the region but it would be between six and seven o'clock in the evening before the heavy snowfall finally made it to the Eastern extremities of Dorset and a further three hours after that before Hampshire, to the west of Southampton was also engulfed in the screaming white maelstrom. It was at that point that the weather fronts would grind to a halt. This would leave everywhere in England and Wales southwest of a line from Aberystwyth to the Isle of Wight in the teeth of the blizzard; with Devon, Somerset and Dorset suffering the very worst of the conditions. The temperatures at ground level across this region were between minus 2°C to minus 4°C and in such very cold temperatures the falling snow became very fine which in turn allowed it to drift very easily in the strong winds.

With the 18th February being a Saturday many people were planning a night out despite the bitter conditions. One such was Richard Wheeler who lived at East Stoke between Wareham and Wool. Richard set out towards Martinstown in his mark one Cortina to pick up his fiancee Sheila for a night out at Weymouth Pavilion. Meanwhile in Martinstown Sheila was waiting for Richard in what she describes as her 'green floaty dress'. Richard was always punctual and never missed a date so it was something of a surprise when he did not turn up at the appointed hour of seven o'clock. Eight o'clock came and went as did nine o'clock and still no Richard. With the heavy snow falling outside all kinds of thoughts went through Sheila's mind. Had Richard had an accident? Had she been stood up? Back in 1978 there were no mobile phones and plenty of homes still didn't have a telephone. A good number of people still used public phone boxes. With no means of getting or receiving a message Sheila waited all evening before going to bed with the blizzard howling outside.

While Sheila had been waiting, Richard had been battling his way through the blizzard. Having got to the western outskirts of Dorchester. He found the way to Martinstown completely blocked by snowdrifts and headed back towards his home at East Stoke.

The blocked road to Martinstown however would prove to be just the first of his problems that evening. Conditions were deteriorating practically by the minute and even the main roads that Richard had travelled along to get as far as Dorchester were by now proving far more difficult to negotiate. After slipping and sliding for several miles on a 'nightmare' journey he finally came to halt in Owermoigne where as luck would have it some friends ran the local garage. Good friends they indeed proved to be after Richard had hammered on their door and explained that he was well and truly stuck and could travel no further.

They took him in and fed him and there he stayed for the next three days helping to clear the garage forecourt once the snow had abated. Meanwhile of course a very worried Sheila was trapped in Martinstown. Richard managed to get the phone number of Sheila's aunt who lived a couple of doors away from her to let her know that he was safe, eating spaghetti at every meal and still wearing his blue 'Saturday night out suit' but also that he didn't know when he would get to see her next. However loves young dream was not to be vanquished, not even by the worst blizzard in a hundred years. Richard and Sheila were married in June 1978.

Many people, especially those looking to retire, move to Dorset for its climate; the usual winter mildness and balmy summer days proving an irresistible draw. It was this and a love of sailing that brought Joyce and Laurie Ingham to the village of Sutton Poyntz on the outskirts of Weymouth in 1976. Such was their obvious enjoyment of the area that a couple of their friends Barry and Nesta, decided to do something along the same lines and mid February 1978 found those friends staying at a Sandbanks hotel whilst they searched for a possible new home. On finding out that Barry and Nesta were staying in the county Joyce and Laurie invited them over for a meal and a date was set. Saturday 18th February!

Late on Saturday afternoon, having left a cloudy but dry Sandbanks Barry and Nesta arrived at the Inghams' home in Old Bincombe Lane but their journey half way across the county was taking them straight towards the blizzard, which by that time was starting to make its presence felt in Sutton Poyntz. Making light of the conditions Joyce jokingly welcomed her guests by saying "don't worry I have made up the spare bed!"

Little did Joyce know just how long that bed would be needed. As late afternoon became early evening and with the snow becoming heavier and starting to drift in the gale force winds it became clear that Barry and Nesta could not attempt to return to Sandbanks. So after a convivial evening and armed with borrowed toothbrushes and night clothes Barry and Nesta settled down to a nights sleep in the spare bedroom thinking that all would probably be well by the morning.

It wasn't just in the south of the county that conditions were worsening. Up in Sherborne, Ray Hazell and his wife were setting out to go to a dinner dance just across the border at the Studios in Yeovil. Having picked up another couple who were joining them they headed west onto the A30. The sleet which had been falling very quickly turned to snow and throughout the dinner people arriving at the venue were commenting on how heavily the snow was falling. Around mid evening the police called into the venue and suggested that due to the severity of the conditions it would make sense for any one who had to travel any distance to make tracks while they still had a chance of getting home. Some left but a good number of people decided to hang on and enjoy the evening.

By half past eleven conditions had deteriorated to the point that road travel had become impossible. Any ideas about sleeping the night at the venue itself were knocked on the head by the management who pointed out that they were not insured to allow that to happen.

Thankfully the kindness of friends led to Ray, his wife and their two companions being offered the chance to stay at a house about a mile away in Yeovil itself. Trekking through a blizzard is all very well if you are equipped for it but trekking through a blizzard when dressed for a dinner dance proved a somewhat different experience for the four friends. Never the less they made it to their overnight shelter where they settled down for the night hoping that conditions would have improved by the morning.

Down in the southeast corner of the county at Canford cliffs, Maureen Smith was waiting for her husband to return from London where he had been working. Her daughter Dawn had already fallen 'victim' to the blizzard conditions and was staying with friends. Arriving by train which terminated at Bournemouth station, Mr Smith headed out into the blizzard and across Bournemouth towards Canford Cliffs. Finally reaching the area around midnight. His arduous trek had clearly not diminished Mr Smith's sense of humour and upon reaching the zebra crossing in Haven Road he took advantage of being the only pedestrian in a traffic free environment. Throwing caution the wind he did the classic Morecambe and Wise jig across the zebra crossing. He certainly brought a little light relief to the situation, because suddenly getting the feeling he was being watched, he looked up to see a couple looking out of a window in fits of laughter at his escapade.

The trials and tribulations of trying to get home in the severest blizzard for years were now becoming a common problem right across Dorset. So much so that in Dorchester, Coburg Road School was opened up as an emergency rest centre at the request of the police.

At the authors recently aquired family home in Worth Matravers heavy snow had started falling at about seven o'clock but it was at about half past nine in the evening that Misty the cat meowed to be let out of the back door. One look at the wall of snow half way up the doorway was enough to make him think better of it, and to make the author realise that this was not like any snowstorm he had seen before.

 "I knew conditions were bad outside simply from the howling wind and the mass of flakes driving past the big picture windows at the front of the house, but finding the deepest snowdrift I had ever seen outside the backdoor really brought home to me just what was going on".

"My brother and I spent the rest of the evening watching as the snow got deeper and deeper seemingly by the minute. However our excitement was tempered somewhat by the knowledge that our parents were dining with friends down in the centre of the village. Although they would normally have walked the quarter mile or so to their friends house, the wind was so bitter when they set off at seven o'clock that they had taken the car but it was becoming obvious that there was no way they would be driving back up the hill to get home."

"Earlier in the evening when our parents had left, the first few crystalline flakes had been snaking across the ground. Now as midnight approached whole drifts of snow now appeared to be gradually moving as the wind screeched in excess of gale force."

"As a family we had only moved into Worth Matravers on the 30th January. My brother and I both being teenagers had not exactly welcomed the idea with open arms having grown up in the relative metropolis that was Bournemouth. Yet here we were, set for real adventure in the wild white wilderness of the Purbeck hills. Just before midnight, guided by a mixture of concern and bravado, my brother and I made our way down the hill towards the centre of the village passing through the cutting outside the Square and Compass pub. Neither of us had ever experienced anything like it. The howling wind was like something one might hear in a movie set in the Arctic! The snow although blowing from behind us was thick in the air and cut visibility dramatically at times. Then of course there were the snowdrifts which by now were already some five feet deep."

"Forging onwards towards the centre of the village entailed wading through thigh deep snow in places before finally reaching the cottage where our parents were dining. Here we were greeted with yet another incredible site, a vast wedge shaped snowdrift stretched from the eaves of the cottage tapering away to about a foot in depth on the opposite side of the street. Some where in the middle of this wedge and completely engulfed in the snow was my father's Morris Marina."

"We let ourselves into the scullery that ran down the side of the cottage and knocked on the kitchen door to be greeted by our parents friends, Ted and Jean. They were shortly joined by our parents. All four had been cocooned away all evening curtains pulled and were totally oblivious to the severity of the conditions outside."

"I told my parents that conditions had worsened somewhat compared to when they had left earlier in the evening and asked how they intended to get home. My father replied that he intended to drive home because the car had front wheel drive and would easily make it back up the hill even through a few inches of snow. It was at this point that I asked him which car he was referring to and if it could possibly be the one that was completely entombed in the eave-deep snow drift in front of the cottage. After a short walk to the scullery door and a few anglo-saxon expressions of astonishment, the decision was taken to walk back up the hill towards home."

"We bid Ted and Jean goodnight and the four of us headed out into the blizzard. The return home which is a walk of some 350 yards took on the feel of an Arctic expedition. The howling gale that had assisted my brother and I down the hill was now screaming straight into our faces and the only way one could make any headway was with one arm raised to protect our eyes from the blasts of needle like snowflakes."

"The hill back towards home was only moderately steep and in normal conditions would do little more than raise the heartbeat slightly but headfirst into a force nine gale and having to work a path through almost waist deep snow made it a very energy sapping experience indeed. It certainly brought home to me how easy it must be for walkers and climbers to become disorientated in unfamiliar mountain territory."

"We were in very familiar territory and yet every step of the way was a struggle in the blinding snow. After about ten minutes of struggling the welcome site of the house reared up through the snow and we tumbled in through the back door; once we had cleared the drift that was fast obliterating it of course. Throughout the struggle home we each had an arm raised in front of our faces to try and protect ourselves from the stinging effects of the storm driven snowflakes. When we took our coats off each of us had a crust of snow on the arm of our coats which was about two inches thick."

"As we warmed up by the range in the kitchen we animatedly discussed the severity of the conditions. My father commented that despite the gale force winds and our relatively remote location "at least the electricity hadn't gone off" barely had the words left his lips before we were plunged into darkness. "Nice one dad."

Throughout the evening people all over Dorset had been battling with the quickly deteriorating situation. Those living in the county at least had the luxury if one can call it that, of knowing what conditions were like. However for those travelling into the county or returning from trips away on that fateful February evening the truly arctic conditions came as something of a shock.

This was the situation that befell Josie and John Pleavin and their two daughters late on that Saturday evening. Having arrived at a frosty but snow free Gatwick Airport after a half term ski-ing holiday the last thing they were expecting was to come home and find more snow in Dorset than they had left behind in Austria. They had learned on their arrival at Gatwick that snow had been forecast for the west country but decided to collect their car and head for their home at Broadmayne.

The majority of the journey passed without incident indeed they saw not a hint of a flake of snow until they were travelling across the New Forest area. They then headed south towards Poole in the hope that closer to the coast the snow might be lighter, which in many cases would probably have been correct, but not on this exceptional evening. Instead the snow got heavier and deeper, so much so that having joined the Upton by-pass to the west of Poole they found themselves unable to go any further. Leaving the car where it was, they headed on foot towards Upton to try and seek refuge at the village pub.

As they trudged through the blizzard a local farmer who had been using his JCB to try and clear some of the snow, saw them and offered them a lift to the pub where they found shelter for the night. They now planned to continue the rest of their journey to Broadmayne the following day. It would however be a journey that would involve three different forms of transport, and one, in which the skis they had been using just forty eight hours earlier in Austria would have proved invaluable.

Elsewhere in the county others were also grinding to a halt but without the advantage of a friendly JCB driver to pick them up. Such was the case of music teacher Roger Smith, his wife and their two children who were returning from London to their home at Lady Bailey Caravan Park near Winterborne Whitechurch. Much as the Pleavins' car had done theirs too became stranded in the drifting snow. This time a mile or so south of Blandford.

The Smith's children were both under five years old. Trudging the final few miles home to Winterborne Whitechurch through the Siberian winds and blasting snow was simply not an option. Fortunately they had four sleeping bags with them in the car and also a small amount of food and settled down for the night and waited to see what the morning would bring.

Across the county in the Pleavins home village of Broadmayne, Arthur and Irene Jeanes, Landlord and Landlady of the Black Dog Pub had been out catering for a Young Farmers event elsewhere in the village and had great difficulty returning to the pub, due to the depth of the snow that had fallen during the evening. They would find themselves catering for a great many more people before the blizzard finally blew itself out.

Meanwhile about six hundred teenagers were enjoying themselves at the town hall disco in central Bournemouth. When the doors opened at seven in the evening just a little light sleet had been falling but this quickly turned to heavy snow and as conditions worsened, those using public transport were advised to "make a break for it" while they could and about four hundred and fifty or so decided to leave at that point. By the time the disco ended later in the evening all roads out of town were blocked by snow, leaving most of those who remained to bed down for the night on the dance floor using old curtains and coats as blankets. There was very little in the way food in the hall but a local hotel helped out with hot soup.

Some brave souls decided not to stay the night and headed out into the blizzard. One such was Beryl Stainer who, spurning accommodation from friends and lifts from the police trekked through the ever deepening snow in the direction of her home in Ensbury Park where her concerned father was waiting up for her. She finally arrived home safe and sound but very cold at about two o'clock on Sunday morning.

Elsewhere in the area teenagers found themselves marooned at the Maison Royale discotheque in Bournemouth and also the Wessex Bowl ten pin bowling centre between Westbourne and Parkstone.

Across the county the worsening conditions found more and more people having to spend the night away from their homes and loved ones.

Yet nothing could have been farther from the minds of the O level and CSE art students from St Mary's School in Puddletown when they boarded their coach to London early on Saturday morning. The purpose of the trip was for the students to visit the Royal Academy to view a collection of Leonardo Da Vinci Drawings that belonged to the Queen.

To round out the day, the afternoon was taken up with a tour of the Inns of Court and the evening with a visit to the Albany theatre to watch a performance of "Oliver". Had they known what sort of weather was brewing back home they might well have given Oliver a miss.

They did however get a hint of what awaited them when they made the obligatory comfort stop at Fleet services on the M3. Asked by a policeman where they were headed, their answer of Dorset was greeted with the reply "You'll be lucky". Undaunted, they continued their journey home but rather like the Pleavins and Smiths ran into atrocious conditions. The journey beyond Southampton being exceptionally slow and difficult. However due to the skill of their driver they somehow against all the odds managed to make it back to Puddletown, arriving at a quarter to midnight.

The tortuous journey was only the start of their difficulties. It was at journeys end where the problems really began. The school had a large rural catchment area and many of those on the trip came from outlying villages that were already completely cut off from the outside world. All pupils and staff who lived outside Puddletown were gathered in the staff room whilst the headmaster and all parents involved were informed. Mattresses from the P.E. store were laid out and the stranded party spent a fitful but exciting night not knowing when they might get home and certainly not thinking for a moment that they were about to become front page news across the nation.

The weather situation in Dorset and the rest of south western England was already making headline news on the television and as midnight came and went it was becoming clear to all concerned, not least the emergency services that an extraordinarily severe weather event was unfolding across the county.

Even with the appalling conditions that had prevailed throughout the evening snowplough drivers reported that some people were still trying drive, in some cases on roads that had already been closed. In other cases drivers were trying to manoeuvre around snowploughs only to get stuck in the drifts a few yards ahead and impede any chance of snow clearance.

It was this crazy behaviour alongside memories of the winter of 1963 when a number of people had died after becoming trapped in a car on Osmington Hill near Weymouth that led Dorset Assistant chief constable Len Burt to take the unprecedented decision to blockade the main towns and some of the larger villages throughout the county.

Most rural villages were already unreachable as the lanes leading to them were filling up with snow and many major roads were becoming indistinguishable from the fields and verges alongside them. Even moving around the larger towns was becoming impossible. Conditions were continuing to deteriorate all the time with the blizzard blowing harder than ever.

To all intents and purposes Dorset was now completely cut off from the rest of England!

Still it blows and still it snows!

Sunday 19th February

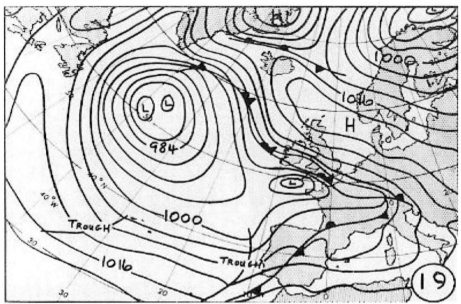

© Crown Copyright - provided by the Met Office

> The pressure map above shows the snow bearing weather front reinvigorated by yet another area of low pressure, lying stationary across Dorset and the south west as the severe blizzard conditions continued across the county during Sunday 19th.

Any one hoping for an improvement in conditions when they woke up on Sunday 19th would be quickly disabused of such thoughts when they drew back their curtains that morning. It was clear that far from abating during the night the blizzard conditions had in fact intensified even further. The authors father on waking that Sunday morning remarked that the snow must have melted away during the night because there was none of that brilliant white light that tries to burst in around the edge of the closed curtains when there's as good covering of snow on the ground in the early morning. It fell to me to tell him that the reason that there was no brilliant white light trying to squeeze in around the edge of the curtains was that the snow was more than halfway up the back wall of the house and had completely buried the window of the ground floor bedroom and more worryingly it was still snowing!

All across the county people were waking up to amazing scenes with massive snowdrifts. The landscape was completely changed. Country lanes that ran between high banks were in many cases filled to the brim while the fields next to them were often practically blown clean of snow. It wasn't just the country lanes either. All the main trunk roads west of Bournemouth were completely blocked. In many cases by drifts up to ten feet deep. Over the more exposed high ground where the winds had been at their worst overnight, drifts between twenty and thirty feet deep were not uncommon.

Some idea of the sheer depth of the drifted snow can be gauged from the author's own experience at Worth Matravers.

" The scenes which met my eyes on the morning of the 19th February 1978 were quite fantastic and will stick in my mind for the rest for my life. I had never seen anything like it before and have seen nothing to compare with it since. On digging my way out of the back door I was greeted with by the sight of a massive drift at the back of the house which started just beneath the windowsill of the first floor bedroom window and ended about halfway across the lawn at the back of the house. Along the side of the house the drifts were shallower just three or four feet deep! and in a sort of wave form. I was joined by my brother and we battled our way down to the road at the front of the house where level snow lay about two feet deep, and headed towards the junction in the cutting just below the Square and Compass public house. The cutting was filled with snow to a depth of seven or eight feet in places. We decided to join the road north out of the village."

The junction outside the Square and Compass pub at Worth Matravers. Picture courtesy Brian Bugler.

"This proved to be an interesting exercise. The road was almost completely buried in huge drifts. There is a high bank on the east side of the road and the snow had piled up here and across the road in the lee of the south easterly gale. The barbed wire fence at the side of the road was somewhere under the drifts which then petered out in the field next to the road Perhaps due to the force of the winds, the drifts were quite hard and compacted and it was possible after a fashion to walk and climb on them. There seemed to be a relative lull in the weather so we scrambled our way on to the top of one of the drifts along the road. It was an exhilarating experience to say the least. Once on top it was possible to walk along with our feet only sinking about six inches into the snow".

"It was while walking along the top of this drift that the sheer scale of this extraordinary weather event really hit home. My foot caught on something in the snow and when I looked down to see what it was, I realised I was looking end on at the top of a telegraph pole! Returning to the house after this adventure the relative lull in the weather took its leave and the wind started to rise again and more snow started to fall. The blizzard was back and making its presence felt in no uncertain terms. Having lost our electricity supply the previous evening, we had now lost our water supply as well. The emergency generators at the pumping station had failed. The snow siege had begun!"

While my brother and I had been enjoying our adventures in the snow that Sunday morning others across the county had far more pressing matters. Not least the police who were now dealing with many reports of people stranded or in need of help. By ten o'clock in the morning an emergency control centre had been set up at the divisional headquarters in Weymouth Avenue at Dorchester. It became clear on that Sunday morning with the blizzard still blowing that nearly all towns and villages west of Poole and Bournemouth were totally cut off by road.

This included the village of Winfrith Newburgh and the nearby Winfrith Atomic reactor where Peter Walker having finished his double shift was trapped. The snowdrifts that had been lapping at the bottom of the boundary fence at Saturday teatime were now as high as the fence itself, some ten to twelve feet. A handful of workers who lived locally at Wool and battled through the terrible conditions arrived, but only to relieve those other locals who had been on shift, meaning Peter had to stay on duty.

He and his fellow 'strandees' had no food and were not allowed to open the canteen on the other part of the site! Eventually on Sunday evening, it was arranged for a tracked vehicle from Bovington Camp to bring in some food, although this was only the basics because they had nothing to cook with. This created an almost surreal situation in which Peter and his fellow workers were supplying megawatts of electricity into the national grid powering cookers all over the UK but were unable to cook anything themselves. Peter's ordeal although eased by a little food was still far from over.

Conditions in the Winfrith area, like these on the road to Lulworth just south of Winfrith Newburgh show why Peter Walker was trapped on shift at the nearby atomic reactor. Pictures courtesy John 'Kiwi' Mays

Meanwhile at Sutton Poyntz, Joyce and Laurie Ingham and their dinner guests Barry and Nesta awoke to find that things weren't any better in the morning and that conditions from the night before had become far more serious. Barry and Nesta certainly weren't going back to their hotel in Sandbanks. The deep drifts ensured that Sutton Poyntz was cut off along with just about every other village in Dorset. The development in Old Bincombe Lane that Mr and Mrs Ingham had moved to was still incomplete so they and their guests got to know their few new neighbours very well, as they all helped each other as best they could. Indeed Barry and Nesta were going to get to know Sutton Poyntz in far more detail than they had bargained for.

Nesta gets to know a blizzard bound Sutton Poyntz in rather more detail than she had bargained for when arriving for dinner with the Inghams the previous evening. Picture courtesy of Joyce Ingham.

The renewed high winds and heavy snowfall did not bode well for the farming community with dairy and sheep farmers suffering the worst. Drifts up to twenty feet deep on many rural roads meant that milk tankers could not get through to pick up the dairy yields and many thousands of gallons had to given away to locals or flushed down the drains.

At Long Bredy, John Thacker and his wife Joan managed a number of dairies for a businessman based in London. They woke up on that Sunday morning to find their farmhouse practically buried.

" The snow was right up to the bedroom windows. We couldn't get out of the house and we had to telephone our son-in-law Ian Wrixon to come over and dig us out. I've never seen anything like it." Reported Mrs Thacker at the time.

Meanwhile the Thackers' own sons worked tirelessly trying to clear a stretch of the A35 and help stranded motorists.

Sheep farmers suffered heartbreaking losses because the huge drifts had buried many ewes just as they were coming up to lambing time. High above Lulworth Cove, close to Durdle Door, farmer Paul Simpson and his mother Ruth lost twenty newborn lambs. The lambing shed was open on two sides one of which unfortunately faced into the teeth of the blizzard. The ewes in the shed had eight inches of snow on their backs and seventy percent of the newborn lambs had succumbed to the cold.

Ruth Simpson spent much of the first night of the blizzard shovelling clear the path between the farm house and the lambing shed. As if this wasn't hard enough she and Paul also had to dig out eleven rams buried in a ten foot drift. The deep drifts had also buried the fences and hedges allowing their herd of heifers to literally walk off the farm! February 19th 1978 was certainly a birthday that Paul Simpson would remember.

In the west of the county at Beaminster, snowdrifts fifteen feet deep buried five hundred sheep on Robert Dupont's farm and despite the best efforts of farm workers and neighbours to dig them out nearly one hundred of them died.

The above are just a few examples of the hardships being endured by the county's agricultural community on that bitter Sunday. To list them all would take another book!

The conditions at Wool are indicative of the sheer depth of snow that fell even in the lower lying towns and villages of south Dorset.
Pictures courtesy of Alan Brown.

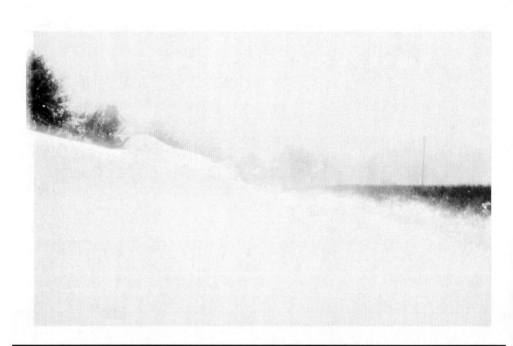

Blizzard conditions can reduce visibility to dramatically as can be seen here as the 'Blizzard of 78' rages around Martinstown on the morning of Sunday 19th . Pictures courtesy Maureen Marchant.

The Smith family, who had spent Saturday night camped out in their car after it ground to a halt in the drifting snow just south of Blandford, awoke to find the blizzard still blowing.

They were however, well, and the sleeping bags and the little food they had with them had kept them going. About twelve hours after their adventure in the snow had begun they were rescued by farm workers and the Police who took them into Blandford where they stayed at the D'amory Arms until conditions allowed them to complete their journey to Winterborne Whitechurch.

It was with typical British understatement that Mrs Smith later described the whole episode as "Rather worrying".

The Pleavins, who had come to a halt on the Upton by-pass to the west of Poole on Saturday evening, had spent a somewhat more comfortable night than the Smiths having managed to make their way with a little help to the village Pub in Upton.

Sunday morning saw them digging their car out of the drift it had run into and picking their way gingerly towards Wareham helped by the fact that some locals had already tried to clear some of the snow from the roads. However Wareham was far as they could get by road and their car was left at the railway station. The family then caught the first available train going west on what was proving to be south Dorset's only lifeline.

The train took them to Dorchester, but this still left them with a five and a half mile walk eastwards to their home at Broadmayne; A walk that would not be possible for their younger daughter who had injured her knee on the ski-ing trip from which they had been returning when they had become stuck. Leaving her with friends in Dorchester, they set out on their snowy trek back to a blizzard-bound Broadmayne.

Several hours later having battled past immense drifts they finally made it home, where yet more snowdrifts were blocking the front of their house.

Despite being taken during the road clearance process. These photographs taken along the main A352 near Broadmayne give some idea of the conditions that the Pleavin family had to battle their way through on their walk home from Dorchester. Pictures courtesy Josie Pleavin, top, and Arthur and Irene Jeanes.

Neighbours had to dig a path to get access to the Black Dog pub at Broadmayne which is hardly surprising when one sees amount the of snow around the building and in the car park. Pictures courtesy of Arthur and Irene Jeanes.

Elsewhere in Broadmayne at the Black Dog pub, the landlords Arthur and Irene Jeanes had awoken to find snow piled high against the windows but some semblance of village life had to carry on and thirsty neighbours dug out paths to the front and rear entrances, and as so often happens in rural emergencies, the pub became the centre of village life.

Luckily, the pub was well stocked with food which was just as well because by the end of Sunday there were some twenty seven people staying on the premises. Amongst them were a Police Seargant , a nurse, soldiers from Bovington army Camp, staff from A.U.W.E at Portland who had been returning from a theatre trip to Bournemouth and a pregnant lady. All of them had become trapped in the massive snowdrifts between Warmwell Cross and Broadmayne.

Police Sergeant David Manuel was amongst those trapped at the Black Dog Pub. Picture courtesy of Arthur and Irene Jeanes.

Going nowhere. The Warmwell Cross Junction (above) and the road from there to Weymouth via Poxwell and Osmington were completely snowed up. Pictures courtesy Arthur and Irene Jeanes.

The pub had three well stocked freezers and plenty of Calor gas for cooking. Heating came courtesy of two coal fires in the public bar and lighting from Calor gas lamps and candles. There were even a few beds for those that required them. Those who were stranded could hardly have found a better safe haven.

The pub came into its own for the locals as a distribution point for milk from a local dairy farm. With the road network unusable, dairy lorries could not get through to make their pick ups from the farm and rather than see it all just poured away the farmer offered it to the pub, which then put the word out on the grapevine. Very soon a queue of people had formed many of whom insisted on paying, despite the fact that that the farmer had waived any payment for the forty gallons that he had given. Landlady Irene had the bright idea of putting the R.N.L.I. collection box on the counter so that people could make a donation as payment and in no time at all it was full

The police sergeant who was trapped at the pub had a radio link to the police headquarters and this would prove vital as the snow siege continued.

Just over the Somerset border in Yeovil, Ray Hazell, his wife and their two companions had spent Saturday night at accommodation kindly offered by friends when the conditions had proved insurmountable after the dinner dance at the Studios. Waking on the Sunday morning to find conditions had deteriorated even further they realised the only way back to their homes at Sherborne would be to walk! So dressed in some borrowed coats they headed across Yeovil and out onto the A30 dual carriageway which had essentially become a skating rink piled high with snowdrifts. The long drag up Babylon hill proved very tough going indeed, the few four wheel drive vehicles that dared to venture out very soon deciding to turn back.

As they continued on their way they passed cars that were buried up to their roofs in snow. After four long and arduous hours hiking through the deep drifts, the Post house hotel and the turning into Horsecastles Lane at

Sherborne came into view about a quarter of a mile ahead. They were nearly home, where they would be welcomed by their neighbours who had looked after the Hazells' sons and then cooked the frozen party a hot meal.

Snowy Sherborne. The knee deep snow shown here at the Conduit was one of the shallower drifts in the town, as the pictures on the following pages will confirm. Picture courtesy Ray Hazell.

The back streets of Sherborne where digging your way out was the only way out! Pictures courtesy Ray Hazell.

Massive drifts sculpted by the gale force winds littered Horsecastles Lane at Sherborne. Note the bus stop sign just sticking out of the drift. Pictures courtesy Ray Hazell.

At St Mary's School in Puddletown the students and teachers who had spent the night sleeping in the school after returning from their trip to London awoke to the worsening conditions and realised they wouldn't be going home anytime soon. One of the teachers, Mr Wrigley, and a small party of boys made their way to Talbots bakery and purchased some supplies to cover their immediate needs, and a hearty breakfast of Cornflakes, Bacon and eggs with toasted rolls and marmalade was served up with mugs of tea and coffee.

During the morning the students kept themselves amused playing cards games, badminton and table tennis. Meanwhile villagers learning of the students' plight, offered to put up those who were stuck away from home and arrangements were made for the students to be billeted at various homes in the village.

Following a lunch of sausages, meat pies and jacket potatoes supplied by the Kings Arms pub, the marooned students were sent to their various billets. Houses with telephones were chosen for ease of keeping the children in contact with their parents and the school. The teachers lodged at the school for a second night and all the while the snow kept falling and the drifts kept growing until by the end of Sunday, the village was encircled by drifts up to twenty feet deep!

A few miles away at Bovington Army camp, yet more people were trapped. Saturday night had seen the annual dinner of some thirty Army cadet force officers and their guests at the Royal Armoured Corps mess. The blizzard conditions and ever deepening drifts ensured that no one could go home so they were put up at the mess. Close by, British legion members enjoying a dinner dance at the memorial hall also found themselves unable to leave and during Sunday fifteen of them were transported to the officers and sergeants messes by an armoured personnel carrier and given rooms in what was fast becoming known as the 'Bovington Hilton'.

In Bournemouth most of the one hundred and fifty youngsters who had been trapped at the town hall disco on Saturday night were taken home by police in four wheel drive vehicles. However with roads to Parkstone, Southbourne and Blandford still blocked at least twenty remained there on Sunday and would be spending a second night camped out there.

Although conditions were not quite as severe as those in rural areas. Bournemouth was nevertheless brought to a standstill by its deepest snowfall on record. Picture courtesy Daily Echo Bournemouth

Movement around Poole on four wheels was difficult enough so it was a brave soul who ventured out on two wheels instead. Nigel Bryant was one such, as these pictures of Poole and his beloved Yamaha XT500 prove.

It's not often you can park a motorbike in the middle of the Towngate bridge in Poole or walk in the middle of Sandbanks Road but the blizzard of 78 ensured that you could do both, for a while at least. Pictures courtesy Nigel Bryant.

Being trapped in a blizzard is bad enough if you are fit and well but if you are unwell or seriously ill and you live a mile or so down a lane then the situation can rapidly escalate into a full scale emergency. It was such a situation that led to young Bernard Hammick of Merley House near Wimborne making front page news in the national press.

Bernard was just fifteen years old and was a boarder at nearby Canford School. After feeling unwell during Friday the 17th, his mother Jo had collected him from school and taken him home to recover. During the night of the 18th as the blizzard raged all around, Bernard's condition worsened dramatically and when he awoke on the 19th he was in a great deal of pain. Mrs Hammick contacted the family doctor, the late Michael Russell, who, after asking her to carry out some basic tests on Bernard, made a diagnosis of suspected appendicitis. Living close to the ambulance station in Wimborne Dr Russell told Mrs Hammick that he would come with the ambulance if he could.

This is were the problems really began. The Hammicks home, Merley House, is situated one mile up a lane off the main A349 Poole to Wimborne road. The lane was blocked with deep drifts of snow making access impossible.

Mr Hammick donned his skis and set off across the snow to meet Dr Russell at the end of the lane. Dr Russell arrived in a four wheel drive fire tender. He borrowed Mr Hammick's skis and headed up to the house to attend Bernard. Mr Hammick meanwhile walked back to the house to get a digger in order to free the fire tender from a snowdrift in which it had become stuck!

On reaching Bernard, Dr Russell confirmed his diagnosis of appendicitis and also that Bernard must be taken to Poole hospital immediately, but with the fire tender stuck a mile away at the end of the lane the only way to get the seriously ill youngster to hospital would be to carry him out to the tender.

Next problem; How do you carry a seriously ill fifteen year old lad a mile across snowdrifts? The Hammicks suggested that he be carried in the front bucket of the digger but Dr Russell felt this would be too bumpy. The answer to this problem was to make a stretcher by zipping two barbour jackets together turning them inside out and pushing boat oars down the sleeves!

Young Bernard was wrapped in sleeping bags and rugs to keep out the bitter cold, laid on the makeshift stretcher and carried out to the tender by the six firemen. The deep snow led to many a fall on the way back to the tender into which Bernard was loaded. A slow and very tricky journey to Poole saw Bernard arrive at Poole hospital four hours after the tender had arrived at the entrance to Merley House.

Safe at last? Well not quite. After starting the operation the doctor on duty could not find Bernard's appendix and had to call in a senior surgeon who also had to get to the hospital! Bernard's appendix was eight inches long and had attached itself to his liver making the operation far more serious than a run of the mill appendicectomy. Bernard remained in hospital for over a week and his story made the front pages of the national press. He thankfully made a full recovery and is now married with two children. According to his mum he still bemoans the fact that his appendix stopped him enjoying the biggest snowstorm of his life!

Bernard was in some ways quite lucky because although he lived somewhat out on a limb he was at least still relatively close to the Poole / Bournemouth conurbation and the services that he needed. Things can be a whole lot different when you live on a farm at Fontmell Magna in the hills of north Dorset. Alice Woodward lived at Middle Farm bungalow and was heavily pregnant. With amazing timing her baby decided that the best time to arrive would be in a raging blizzard with ten foot deep snowdrifts cutting you off from the outside world.

The severity of the Blizzard conditions meant that a helicopter rescue had to be called off and even the combined efforts of five police officers two ambulance men and a doctor failed to get through.

Luckily Mrs Woodward was not alone. Her husband Laurence and her cousin Sally Phipps who had attended a birth before were at the bungalow with her. With their help she gave birth to her son William on the bedroom floor. Mr Woodward kept up a telephone link with Odstock Hospital in order that they could cut the cord at the right time and later in the day the district nurse who lived in the village manage to get through to check that all was well with mum and her newborn son.

Despite the ferocity of the blizzard the railway line between Bournemouth and Weymouth had remained just about open but even this was now getting into trouble as passengers on the 12:48 from Bournemouth to Weymouth found out during Sunday afternoon. The train had managed to battle most of the way across the snowy wastes of south Dorset and was approaching the Bincombe Tunnel which runs under the Ridgeway escarpment to the north of Weymouth when it became stuck in deep drifts that were building across the line.

Thankfully the heating on the train was working as around a hundred passengers waited patiently for a total of three locomotives to come out from Weymouth and breach the drifts so that they could finally make it through, arriving in Weymouth at 6:15pm. Some five and a half hours late!

In the west of the county at Bridport, it was being reported that every road out of the town was blocked by drifts up to twenty feet deep. News which gave little hope of getting home to three different parties of people who had become trapped there since the blizzard hit on Saturday . At the West Mead hotel in the town were two coach loads of theatre goers from Dorchester who had been returning from a trip to Exeter on Saturday when they became marooned as the ever deepening snowdrifts encircled the town. Also trapped in the town were a civic party from Portsmouth including the Lord Mayor, Mr George Austin and his wife who had been trapped by the worsening conditions as they returned from Plymouth having attended the re-commissioning of Portsmouth's adopted warship the frigate HMS Sirius. Not even the finest British engineering in the form of the official Rolls Royce Silver Phantom could get them through and so they too were lodged at the West Mead Hotel.

Elsewhere in the town a party of fishermen from Plymouth who had planned to take part in all night fishing competition were set to spend the second of three nights taking refuge in St Johns Church. The good folk at the Bridport Arms Hotel allowed them to use washing facilities and also supplied them with breakfast and supper. This was a kindness that was reciprocated when the party turned out to help locals clear snow at the old peoples accommodation at Court Orchard and also at a centre for learning difficulties in Flood Lane.

The situation on the railways became increasingly difficult on Sunday 19th as shown in this picture from a line in North Dorset. Picture courtesy of Dorset Echo.

As Sunday evening drew in, Dorset remained very much in the grip of the snow. The continuing high winds and further heavy snowfall had left most towns and villages cut off from each other by drifts that were commonly between ten and fifteen feet deep and in some cases on exposed or high ground the well over twenty feet deep.

The superhuman efforts of the small army of council snowplough drivers, and farmers were often hampered by the high winds. No sooner would they clear a section of road before it would start to fill in again behind them as the wind blew lying snow back across the carriageways and this was just were the snow was shallow enough to be ploughed, Drifts of ten and twenty feet were a different matter altogether and would need to shifted by diggers.

Through Sunday evening into the early hours of Monday 20th the blizzard at last blew itself out but the record breaking snowfall would leave Dorset very much a marooned county. In some places it had snowed for thirty hours with barely a break. The sheer amount of snow that had fallen ensured that it would be the end of the week before the situation across the whole county was back to anything like normal.

The snow had finally stopped falling but now the digging had to begin!

Whiteout at Winfrith

Portrait of a village in the snows

The village of Winfrith Newburgh was as badly affected as any village in the county, a record of the conditions there was made by John 'Kiwi' Mays who took over fifty photographs on the day after the blizzard. Here are just a selection starting in the village High street before moving down to look at conditions on the roads running south from the village to Lulworth Cove and East Chaldon.

Looking south along the High Street from a point opposite the village hall.

Views looking south along the high street towards St Christopher's church (top) and northwards along the same section of the street.

Extensive drifting left many Winfrith residents having to dig their way out of their cottages.

The southern end of the high street with major drifting in the lee of the houses on the left while by the front of the houses on the right the snow has been blown clear.

The top picture shows the view north from the southern end of the High street. Taken from the same point, the picture below shows the view looking east past St Christopher's Churchyard and along the road towards Lulworth Cove.

Heading southeast out of the village and the extreme nature of the drifting on the road to Lulworth Cove becomes immediately apparent.

The amazing effects that the gale force winds had on the drifting snow can be seen above. Somehow the photographer managed to get past the immense drifts to take a shot of the village sign a little further along the road.

Deep drifts as far as the eye can see block the road to Lulworth Cove.

The road from Winfrith to East Chaldon was completely blocked after the blizzard.

The big dig out

Monday 20th - Friday 24th February

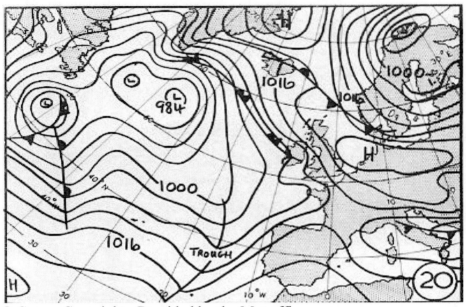

© Crown Copyright - Provided by the Met office.

The pressure map above shows how by noon on Monday 20th the snow bearing weather front that was across Dorset and the southwest has decayed and also that the high pressure that had been feeding in bitterly cold air for the past two weeks is also starting to decline.

Dawn on Monday 20th and the start of the new working week saw Dorset in what can only be described as a state of chaos. For any one living east of Southampton the situation further west must have seemed quite incredible. The severe blizzard conditions had only really affected the south western quarter of England and although conditions in western Hampshire and the New Forest were very difficult with deep snow and considerable drifting, it was in Dorset, Devon and Somerset where conditions were extremely severe. Dorset was essentially a closed county, Almost every 'A' road was blocked or had been closed by the police to enable clearing to begin without any more drivers getting stuck and adding to the chaos. Assistant chief constable Len Burt explained. "It's a thankless task but we feel it is necessary if the council workmen are to be given a chance to clear the roads". He went on to describe the situation as " a white living hell". A phrase which was reprinted in newspapers across the world as the story of Dorset and its monstrous snowstorm was reported as far a field as New Zealand, the U.S.A. and South Africa. A few journalists from some of the national newspapers based in London questioned whether the Assistant chief constable should have been able to take the decision to blockade the towns and villages to aid the road clearance and rescue efforts.

It wasn't just the rural areas where normal traffic movement was impossible as this picture from the county town of Dorchester shows.
Picture courtesy of Margaret Crowther.

The 'white living hell' trapped vehicles on major roads all across the county. As can be seen above on the A352 Dorchester to Sherborne Road and below at Basan Hill on the A354 Blandford to Puddletown road. Pictures courtesy Dorset Echo (above) and Norman Wellstead.

They were quite rightly given short shrift by Len Burt who pointed out to them that he had taken an oath to the Queen to protect life and property and this is exactly what he was seeking to do. The journalists were, after all, in their offices in London which was totally unaffected and didn't have any real idea of what the conditions were like on the ground in Dorset and the west country.

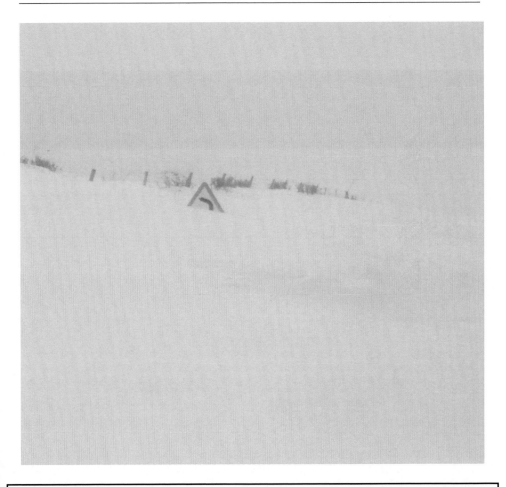

Journalists in an unaffected London who questioned the need for the blockade had no real idea of what conditions were like on the ground in Dorset. This example is from Martinstown. Picture courtesy Maureen Marchant.

These views looking north (above) and south along Weymouth Avenue in Dorchester confirm just how severe conditions were in towns all over the county. Pictures courtesy Margaret Crowther.

Johns Arctic Walk

Despite the still bitterly cold conditions and the fact that massive snowdrifts littered the county some hardy souls decided that if they couldn't drive to work they would try walking in instead. One such conscientious employee was John Hodgson who worked as a draughtsman at County Hall in Dorchester for the valuation and estates department. He set off from his home in Weymouth at about half past eight in the morning and arrived for work at county hall some three and a half hours later.

John had taken up photography as a hobby about eighteen months before the Blizzard of 78 and thanks to this we have a stunning and unique record of Johns Arctic walk from Weymouth to Dorchester via the Ridgeway.

On the long pull up the first leg of the Ridgeway hairpin some semblance of snow clearing is taking place but this would be the last snow clearing vehicle John saw in action until he reached Dorchester.

John rounds the hairpin and leaves the snow plough behind before looking ahead to get his first glimpse of the daunting conditions that await him further up the hill.

The drifted snow just keeps getting deeper as John approaches the cutting towards the top of the hill, note how the fence posts on the left in the top picture are barely sticking out of the snow in the bottom picture as the cutting gets closer.

As John enters the cutting, the drifts on the right hand side start to take on fantastical shapes and rise close to twenty feet above the road giving the appearance of veritable tsunami of snow!

John sets his camera for a delayed shot and walks ahead with the drifts towering above him and contorting themselves into even more amazing shapes

John heads towards the end of the cutting but the drifts just seem to get deeper before he leaves the borough of Weymouth and Portland behind and heads towards Dorchester. Note the welcome to Weymouth sign on the left hand side in the bottom picture.

Nearing the end of the cutting John finds some short lived relief from the monstrous drifts that have dogged his passage along the Ridgeway before yet another massive drift renders the turning to Broadmayne almost invisible.

John meets another 'commuter' on their way to work in Dorchester. Cross country skiing comes into its own as John's fellow commuter races ahead of him across the drifts.

The road to Dorchester disappears into the distance with the drifted snow now merely hedge deep, but hedge deep was more than enough to trap these vehicles including a snowplough/gritting lorry.

John finally gets a distant view of Dorchester after battling his way past yet another massive drift.

The views along High West Street (above) and High East Street (below).
Rarely can Dorchester ever have been so quiet on a working day.

Luckily the railway link between Dorchester and Weymouth had been restored during the day so John did not have to walk all the way back home to Weymouth, although drifts on the platform at Upwey station were almost as high as the train itself!

The big dig out (continued)

At Puddletown, Deputy Headmaster Norman Wellstead had spent a second night sleeping at St Marys School, while those students trapped in the village since Saturday night had spent the night at various billets offered by the villagers. Inspecting the School grounds he found that a general depth of about a foot of snow had fallen but that in places this had been whipped up into drifts between six and ten feet deep. He busied himself during the morning by contacting all the marooned children and also their worried parents. He was contacted by the police who offered help with food and blankets if necessary. They also noted the names of the trapped pupils and their homes.

Norman also received another phone call that morning and this one was to catapult the village and the school into the headlines. Puddletown, and St Mary's School were about to become front page news! The call was from Daily Mail news reporter Peter Cliff saying he planned to visit them by helicopter later that day!

The trapped children were assembled at the school and the school flag was laid on the snow out between the goalposts and the cricket practice area. At about four o'clock amidst great excitement, the helicopter landed with the reporter and a photographer aboard. The helicopter was too small to take any more passengers so there was no rescue for the stranded students. Sure enough the following day saw Norman and the students emblazoned across the front page of the Daily Mail, their ordeal preserved for posterity.

After their brief taste of excitement it was back to their billets for the students. One of the teachers Mr Wrigley was taken towards his home by a tractor but had to complete his journey by walking across the fields. Meanwhile Norman and his colleague Mr Rawlinson settled down for a third night sleeping at the school.

Students and teachers welcome the Daily Mail helicopter as it comes in to land on the playing field at St Mary's School in Puddletown. Picture courtesy of Bournemouth News and Picture service.

A view of a snow bound St Mary's School Puddletown from the Daily Mail helicopter as it circles before coming into land (Above) and Deputy Headmaster Norman Wellstead (front right) with fellow staff Sheila Macdonald, Ann Mulligan, John Wrigley and the stranded students. Pictures courtesy Bournemouth New and Picture Service.

The Puddletown students weren't the only children marooned away from home on that Monday morning. On Portland, fifteen children from London and Southampton were trapped at Portland bird observatory. The children aged between twelve and fifteen had arrived there on Friday night and became trapped as the blizzard howled around them through the weekend. They were however said to be in good spirits and had plenty of food.

Further west at Burton Bradstock seven members of a church youth group from Bournemouth were well and truly trapped at Othona Church of England community house where they had gone to spend a working weekend. They were completely cut off and were told by the police that there was little hope of getting them out in the foreseeable future and that it could well be the following weekend before they would get home!

Also completely cut off were the boys at Milton Abbey School in Milton Abbas. A third of the teaching staff who worked at the boarding school could not get to work and the boys were helping the remaining teachers to run the school.

The police force had a problem of its own to deal with as well. Officers living in rural areas could not get in to work. They were ordered instead to organise local assistance in villages in their areas.

Throughout the weekend, many homes in rural areas had lost power as lines had become iced up or damaged by the severe gales. Portland, Bovington, Wool and Broadmayne to name but a few. Power workers had worked in atrocious conditions throughout Sunday to try and restore some of the supplies. Indeed those who went to try and restore power at Bovington had travelled on a snowplough along the rail track from Weymouth to Wool and then been taken from there to Bovington Camp by a Scorpion Tank! Further east, Studland, Swanage, Corfe Castle and Worth Matravers had already been without power for thirty six hours and Monday saw crews being helicoptered into some of the worst hit locations in Purbeck and also to the line between Maiden Newton and Puncknowle.

Conditions in Mid Dorset around Blandford were extremely difficult with all roads out of the town blocked. At Blandford Army Camp a state of Emergency was declared with the Garrison Commander issuing the following bulletin:

EMERGENCY BULLETIN NO 1

GENERAL

1. There is no movement of traffic in the Blandford Area

2. Unless you have to go out, stay at home.

3. Work is in progress to clear the route through the camp.

4. All work is being controlled from HQ School regiment; Exts 232 233 or 235. This is also the information centre.

FOOD STUFFS

5. Assistance has been requested to fly in essential supplies of bread and milk. When it arrives issues will be from the soldiers dining hall. Payment will be in cash or an IOU if necessary. You will be required to produce your identity card before any issue will be made.

6. A limited supply of bread rolls will be available from the cookhouse from 1430hrs. There may be some fresh milk for children under 5 yrs but you must bring a container with you.

CONCLUSION

If you have any urgent problems then let an officer or NCO know (there will be plenty of people around) and have it reported to the control cell.

The bleak scene around the quarters at Blandford army camp. Picture courtesy Andrew Symmons.

The police blockade of the roads did at least give councils a chance to start the long battle to clear away the drifts. A job that would last all week in the worst affected areas. Yet even with all their announcements warning people not to travel. Police still found themselves having to admonish foolhardy would be travellers. One of the problems may have been that the urban infrastructure around the Bournemouth and Poole conurbation shielded the local town environment from the very worst effects of the blizzard and so in a sense may have presented a somewhat watered down picture of the conditions compared to those a couple of miles out of town where hedged country lanes were filled to the brim and the drifting was far more extreme. What, in town, may just have seemed like a very deep snowfall was in fact the 'white living hell' that Len Burt had described as soon as one left the comparatively sheltered urban environment behind.

The councils at both town and county level threw everything they possibly could at the clearing operations. In Bournemouth alone some two hundred men were set to work, whilst Dorset county council had 150 pieces of plant at work, but the task was immense. You can't clear a twenty feet deep snowdrift just using a gritting lorry with a snowplough on the front. A great deal of the work in rural areas required diggers and bulldozers to be used to shift the snow. A case of quite literally digging out Dorset.

While all this digging was going on the normal difficulties that life throws at people carried on being visited upon the good folk of Dorset. People still fell ill and required a visit from the doctor even if they were to all intents an purposes cut off from the outside world. Near Winfrith an ingenious method of getting the local Doctor to one of his seriously ill patients was devised, namely putting the good doctor aboard a Scorpion Tank and smashing a way through or over the drifts! Elsewhere in the county a number of doctors donned skis to complete their rounds.

A Scorpion tank passes through East Knighton as it delivers the local doctor to a patient near Winfrith. Picture courtesy Noreen Guy.

As the following series of photographs show. In the first few days after the blizzard of 78 had blown itself out, all around the county is it was case of dig dig dig; Whether it was the council workmen with their diggers, gritters and snowploughs. Farmers with their tractors. The army with tanks or Joe Public with a shovel!

A digger gets to work clearing the snow at Godmanstone. Picture courtesy Mrs D Wheeler.

Weymouth is normally one of the most snow-free locations in the UK but in 1978 it had to be dug out along with the rest of the county as shown above at Littlemoor Road and also below at the Ridgeway. Pictures courtesy Margaret Byrne, above, and Mr R Beggs, below.

Diggers get to work clearing the road linking East Chaldon with the A352 near Winfrith. Pictures courtesy John "Kiwi" Mays.

The road from Wool to Lulworth Cove was completely blocked until these bulldozers got to work in the days following the blizzard. Pictures courtesy John Dunk.

Gritters fitted with snowploughs at the Longburton Depot prepare to force a way through the immense drifts on the on the A352 (below) some three or four days after the blizzard. Pictures courtesy Graham Bendell.

A site very rarely seen on Dorset roads as a snowblower gets to work on the main A37 road between Dorchester and Yeovil in the vicinity of the Sydling St Nicholas Junction. Picture courtesy Graham Bendell.

Just two examples of the many abandoned and buried vehicles which hampered the snow clearing operations. These were on the B3145 just to the north of Sherborne. Pictures courtesy Graham Bendell.

If the snowplough hasn't got through to you yet then as these residents of Godmanstone showed, it's basically down to you and your shovel.
Pictures courtesy Mrs D Wheeler.

The scenes in North street (above) and South Street at Wareham as a digger gets to work and the locals come out from under the snow.
Pictures courtesy Ken Ayres.

Severe drifting on the Worgret Road (A352) and the Wareham causeway (below) meant movement east or west from Wareham was out of the question in the days immediately after the blizzard. Pictures courtesy of Ken Ayres.

On Monday morning a locomotive fitted with a snowplough made its way down the mainline from Bournemouth to Weymouth to inspect conditions and clear any drifts. This having been carried out successfully, the first passenger train of the day into Weymouth was the 1:15pm service from Bournemouth. Trains leaving Weymouth later in the day carried milk and bread into Dorchester and outlying villages along the line. It was noted that when the trains reached Upwey station, the doors could not be opened because the snow on the platform was as deep as the train itself!

With the road system out of action all across the county, navy helicopters from the base at Portland came into their own, responding to emergency situations as they developed. They flew fourteen separate missions during Monday 21st these included carrying blood samples from Dorchester to Weymouth and District hospital, delivering insulin to a diabetic at Compton Valence and dropping off food for a baby at Milborne St Andrew. The helicopters also brought relief to the pregnant lady who had been trapped at the Black Dog pub in Broadmayne as can be seen below.

Picture courtesy Arthur and Irene Jeanes.

She, along with a number of the other stranded travellers were airlifted to safety. Those whose weren't flown out were taken out by tracked army vehicles from Bovington camp.

In addition to their blockade the police requested that major employers in the area ask any employees who lived well away from the workplace to stay away from work until conditions had improved. The management at the Winfrith Atomic energy establishment did just this giving One thousand eight hundred employees the day off while two hundred staff essential to the running of the plant were asked to get to work if at all possible. Many of those who had been on shift with Peter Walker when he became trapped at the plant on Saturday night remained at work and would not get home until Wednesday!

Living with the results of the blizzard was difficult for those who had all the mod cons that were around in 1978, but imagine if you had to live in a thatched hut in the middle of nowhere with no central heating or running hot water. A year before the blizzard the BBC had set up five couples to live for a year in an Iron Age settlement near Shaftesbury in what was probably one of the first ever reality TV series.

A BBC spokesman (no doubt speaking from a nice warm office) said.

" They are probably coping better than the 20th Century inhabitants of the snowbound west country. They are certainly warm because in their hut is a fire that is kept burning all the time and they are wearing layers of rough woollens topped off with a few furs."

"All they have to go out side for is to check on the animals, since all the harvest is in. They have special iron age shoes" continued the spokesman, " but they have said they would give anything for a pair of Wellingtons."

" They have no problems with power cuts because they don't have any power and they use natural water sources so that's ok too"

Blizzard Fun

The week leading up to the blizzard had been the half term holiday, allowing the children of Dorset to enjoy the results of the snowfalls on the 15th and 16th before the main blizzard at the weekend. Now to their absolute delight the County education officer announced that all Dorset schools would be closed until at least Wednesday 22nd when another assessment of the situation would take place. So not only did the county's youngsters have a never to be forgotten winter wonderland but were officially granted time off to go out and play in it! With many adults unable to go to work, though, it wasn't just the children who got to mess about in the snow.

No doubt these youngsters at Overcombe drive in Weymouth now tell their own children that they can remember a time when the snow was so deep it was halfway up the lamp posts! Picture courtesy Brian Searle.

Jo Mullen found mountains of snow to play in at Littlemoor on the outskirts of Weymouth. Pictures courtesy Jo Mullen.

Messing about in the snow on the Ridgeway. Pictures courtesy Pat Middle.

When it comes to scooting across the snow you can't beat a sledge. Horse drawn or otherwise. Pictures courtesy Pat Middle, top, and Mr R Beggs.

Julie Kent enjoys a slide in the snow before uncovering a car that had been completely buried near West Fleet Farm to the west of Weymouth. Pictures courtesy of Julie Kent.

The Big Dig out (continued)

In the North and West of Dorset conditions were extremely difficult especially for towns and villages set down in deep valleys. Beaminster was completely cut off from the night of Saturday 18th until Wednesday 22nd despite the best efforts of council workmen who were working from five o'clock in the morning until eight o'clock in the evening.

Locals in west Dorset reported that conditions were worse than in the great winter of 1963, stating that the snow was deeper and the drifting more severe. The snow on the roads either side of Beaminster was up to fifteen feet deep! Many residents found themselves without water after the local pumping station failed when it lost power. The fact that it came back on at all during the week after the blizzard was thanks to Wessex Water engineers who on Tuesday 21st waded through massive drifts for four hours to get the pumps back on and refill the Tollerdown Reservoir.

On the same day three hundred loaves were delivered by tractors to villages around Dorchester and a combined operation involving the navy, police and local farmers also saw bread taken across the snowy wastes to Portesham and Abbotsbury.

Tuesday also brought another problem to the county. By now much milder air was starting to move in from the west which on the one hand did help to start a very slow thaw but the milder air coming into contact with freezing surface of the deep snow created fog limiting the work of the navy helicopters that had been proving so vital in the recovery.

It only takes a relatively shallow layer of fog to render the landscape unrecognisable from the air and this turned out to be the case when one of the navy helicopters was called out to Piddlehinton to the aid of Angela Grist who had gone into labour and appeared to be having complications with the birth. Initially an ambulance tried to get through to the village but could not get through the deep drifts. The helicopter was then scrambled but was unable to locate the Grists' farmhouse and so a team including a Paediatrician, Obstetrician and a staff nurse from Dorset County Hospital at Dorchester headed out towards Piddlehinton in a land rover which was then towed through the drifts by a tractor. Meanwhile retired Doctor James Will walked six miles through the snow to reach Mrs Grist and delivered her baby boy safe and sound just minutes before the team from the hospital arrived. Nicholas Grist weighed in at a very healthy nine and a half pounds.

Yet another form of transport was called in to play on that Tuesday as the fog shrouded so many parts of the county. The coastal village of Ringstead was without electricity and cut off by snowdrifts some thirty feet deep. Electricity board engineers needed to get to the village to check out what work was needed to restore the supply. There was only one way in and that was by sea, so fisherman Brian Randell took a team of four Southern Electricity board staff across Weymouth Bay and landed them on the beach along with Dorset Echo reporter Andrew Wyllie.

Andrew spoke to Freda Fisher who lived in the village with her husband Michael, son Mark and daughter Nicola.

"It was really frightening." reported Mrs Fisher as she recounted the moment when the blizzard hit on the Saturday.

"Everyone made a rush for the hill and there were cars everywhere trying to reach the top of the hill before the snow settled."

The cars that didn't quite make it were buried under thirty feet of snow. The Fisher family had no electricity and were camping out on mattresses in the front room and cooking on a small gas fire.

After spending the morning restoring the supply and checking lines and fuses for damage, the fishing boat returned the electricity board staff to Weymouth along with two extra passengers. Elizabeth Wigzell and her boyfriend had come to the village on Saturday and found themselves trapped when the ferocious blizzard hit.

Meanwhile back at Puddletown, Norman Wellstead was still trapped along with a number of the students from Saturdays trip to London; a load lightened a little perhaps by the news that he, along with his colleagues and the students, now adorned the front cover of the Daily Mail. Fellow teacher Ron Wrigley, who had been given a lift towards his home the previous evening, telephoned to say that he had made it back safely at eight o clock after completing the journey by going across the fields. Another of his colleagues, Ann Mulligan, was able to get home to Dorchester because the A35 was now passable to emergency traffic. Meanwhile during a walk to Basan Hill along the main A354 towards Blandford, Norman saw some of the many vehicles that were still buried by snowdrifts drifts which were up to fifteen feet deep.

As Wednesday 22nd February dawned, a slight improvement had taken place on the roads especially in the eastern half of the county where the A350 between Poole and Blandford and the A351 between Poole and Swanage via Wareham were declared open to all traffic.

Three of the five Puddletown students who were still trapped there were able to make a break for it by hitching a lift to Dorchester under the emergency conditions. They were picked up from there by land rover and taken safely home and finally, at long last, after four nights camping out at the school Norman Wellstead and his colleague Mr Rawlinson were able to get home after being given a lift along the now partially cleared A354 to Winterborne Whitechurch and walking the final few miles across the snow to Winterborne Stickland.

The main A35 road between Bournemouth and Dorchester was open but only to emergency traffic. The section further west between Dorchester and Bridport was under the same restriction although it appears that the two coach parties of theatre goers who had been marooned along with the Lord Mayor of Portsmouth at the West Mead Hotel in Bridport were allowed passage and arrived back in Dorchester four days later than planned. They had nothing but praise for their hosts in Bridport.

Elsewhere The A354 Dorchester to Weymouth road via the Ridgeway was still blocked, as was the A351 Weymouth to Warmwell Cross road via Osmington hill. The blocking of Osmington hill struck a strong chord amongst local people because fifteen years earlier in the historic severe winter of 1963 a middle aged couple from Dorchester had died when the car they were travelling in had become buried under twelve feet of snow in a blizzard.

To the north of Dorchester the A37 to Yeovil and the A352 to Sherborne were still blocked. One wonders how people would cope in today's 'must have it now' society where people can't seem to cope with a few inches of snow closing a road for a few hours let alone four days.

In the east of the county the situation on many minor roads was still very difficult with remote or outlying villages still cut off from the outside world in terms of normal traffic. This situation led to an armoured personnel carrier being used to aid the rescue of an elderly lady who had collapsed in her home at West Morden. The ambulance was unable to get beyond Wareham and with the personnel carrier from Bovington camp leading the way through the drifts the ambulance was towed by a tractor to within a hundred yards of the lady's home. The ambulance was eventually able to drive back to Poole hospital where despite the best efforts of everyone involved the poor lady passed away a day later.

There was some good news at last for Peter Walker who had been trapped on shift at Winfrith Atomic Power station since Saturday afternoon. He was able to get home by train, feeling absolutely exhausted, very hungry and cold. His reward for being trapped at work for the best part of five days was that he was expected to go back to work on Thursday to pick up his usual 2-10 shift!

Once the severity of the situation facing the south-west had been recognised the government of the day appointed Dennis Howell as the "Snow Minister." Mr Howell had already gained a reputation as something of a meteorological minister having been appointed the "drought Minister" in the searing hot summer of 1976 a couple of years earlier.

Mr Howell had intended to visit Dorset on Tuesday 21st but the fog that had hampered the helicopter rescue crews had also prevented him from landing in the county. However Wednesday held no such problems and he arrived for a conference at Dorchester Police Headquarters with officials who were masterminding the battle to put the county back on its feet. Mr Howell spent an hour or so with the local officials ascertaining the current situation and any ongoing needs.

Heading back to London after the meeting Mr Howell told local pressmen that he would be preparing a report for the Prime minister and that he would be making a statement to the parliament the following day.

That statement read as follows

Mr. Speaker, I should like to make a statement upon the emergency situation in the West Country caused by an average of 18 inches of snow which fell last weekend, causing drifts of up to 30 feet and completely blocking communications over a wide area. The local authorities immediately established emergency operational centres to coordinate the actions of the agencies.

I cannot speak too highly of the work of all the services, both public and voluntary. The magnitude of their task can be judged by the fact that some 25,000 houses were without electricity, 100,000 premises were without water, telephone services to 10,000 subscribers were disrupted, and almost all road and rail lines were severed.

On behalf of the Government, I established three priorities: maximum help for people at risk, such as the elderly, the sick and the isolated; to ensure essential supplies of food, water, fuel and feeding stuffs for farm livestock; the restoration of all communications.

As the House would expect, the Armed Services mobilised their resources with first-class efficiency and met every call made upon them. In particular, helicopters provided an emergency ambulance service and transported essential workers to restore vital services.

The Ministry of Agriculture established separate operational centres and received over 200 calls from farmers specifically requesting help in feeding livestock, apart from many more seeking advice on emergency problems. As soon as the fog lifted, 28 helicopters operated this special relief service and are still continuing these duties.

The House will be interested to learn that just one farm in North Devon received 45 tons of feeding stuff yesterday to sustain 400,000 chickens, 2,000 pigs and 200 dairy cattle, and will continue to receive 20 tons per day while the emergency lasts.

The House will wish to know the up-to-date position in the West Country at noon today. Electricity supplies have been restored to all but 1,500 homes. One thousand homes are still without piped supplies of water. Telephone services are returning slowly to normal, but this work has been delayed by the flooding of underground cables, and some 8,000 subscribers are still without service.

All rail passenger services have been restored and most of the major trunk roads are now open except for the north-south routes through Dorset. Snow clearing work is proceeding rapidly. The flood warning system is fully operational and is coping well with the present rate of thaw.

In Wales the situation continues to improve as the thaw progresses. There were two successful airlifts yesterday of fodder and plastic milk containers. There has been one request so far today for a fodder airlift which is being considered. Milk collection difficulties are now confined to a few areas only. A general thaw and heavy rain during the night have helped to clear the roads and only a few villages in the Vale of Glamorgan and South Pembrokeshire remain inaccessible.

As the House will know, my right hon. Friend the Minister of Agriculture made an immediate announcement that, subject to the approval of Parliament, the cost of this airlift will be met by central Government funds. I have also advised my right hon. Friend that the nature of the losses to farmers appears to fall into three categories: the death of animals, the destruction of buildings, and loss of income, particularly from milk. It is far too early for the farming community to calculate those costs but my right hon. Friend is already considering the implications.

So far as local authority emergency expenditure is concerned, I can confirm the statement made by my right hon. Friend the Secretary of State for the Environment on 8th February, in respect of the floods and gales of last November and January, that the Government will pay 75 per cent. of all such emergency expenditure in excess of a penny rate.

Finally, the people of the West Country and Wales have good cause to be grateful to the entire work force engaged in this operation—local authority road men, electricity, water, telephone and transport workers, doctors, Health Service and social service personnel, public servants of both central and local government doing the less spectacular but vital organisational work, and, most important, the Service men and police. Everyone did a wonderful job, sometimes working non stop around the clock for two or three days. I know that the whole House will wish to join in that tribute to them.

The road clearing duties carried on apace into Wednesday night and by Thursday morning the Dorset Echo was able to run the headline. " Most roads now open". The combination of much milder temperatures and the heroic efforts of the snow clearing crews finally saw the A35 from Dorchester to Bridport opened to all traffic as well as the A354 from Weymouth to Dorchester and the A351 eastwards from Weymouth over Osmington Hill.

Yet despite those heroic efforts. Some five days after the blizzard, several main roads were still impassable. The A37 north from Dorchester to Yeovil was still closed between Grimstone and Stockwood and the road west from the A37 going to Crewkerne via Maiden Newton, the A356, was still blocked.

Further east the A354 between Blandford and Puddletown remained closed to normal traffic as did the main A350 north from Blandford to Shaftesbury.

The roads still giving trouble were essentially those that ran across the higher ground and therefore received the deepest snowfall as well as being exposed to the strongest winds, a combination leading to massive drifting of the snow during the blizzard.

Many farms on the higher ground were still cut off and Navy helicopters were needed to bring in fodder for animals. Farms at Toller Pororum and Chilfrome in the cut off area to the north west of Maiden Newton were just two who had help in this way. The flight to Toller Porcorum also being used to airlift a pregnant lady from there to hospital in Dorchester.

As the working week wore on and the much milder conditions helped the county to ease its way out of its snowy prison, thoughts turned to just how the whole clear up and rescue bill was going to be paid for. The bill for road clearing in the county alone was expected to run close to half a million pounds which although today would barely pay a premiership footballer for a month, was nevertheless a huge amount of money back in 1978 . Across the southwest as a whole the bill for damage caused by the blizzard and the subsequent flooding was provisionally put at between five and ten million pounds.

The south-easterly gales that had accompanied the blizzards over the weekend had allowed the seas to give the coastal defences of Dorset a considerable pounding and at West Bay a stretch of the esplanade was severely damaged. This and further damage sustained in 1979 would eventually lead to a bill of six hundred thousand pounds to put things right.

Another unexpected bill was that for the damage done to trees by the severe gales and the weight of snow in parks and gardens in towns across the county.

Farming losses across the southwest region as a whole were massive. Up to thirty thousand ewes were lost and about forty thousand lambs succumbed to the cold and snow. Dairy farmers lost an estimated half a million pounds in lost production with between three hundred thousand and five hundred thousand gallons being lost in Dorset alone. Market gardeners lost out to the tune of a quarter of a million pounds in lost crops and damaged buildings. While damage to other farm buildings from the severe gales and weight of snow accounted for another two hundred and fifty thousand pounds.

A week after the blizzard a new weather induced problem was also threatening the county. A combination of the continuing thaw of lying snow, together with gales and high tides led to flooding. The huge extra amount of water going into the rivers was being held up by exceptionally high tides along the coast and both the Frome and Stour valleys were flooding quite severely. On the coast itself Portland in particular was feeling the brunt with high winds sending the sea over the top of Chesil Beach and flooding the lower lying parts of the Isle. At Preston on the outskirts of Weymouth the road became blocked, this time by drifts of pebbles hurled over the top of the sea wall.

At Worth Matravers in the Purbeck Hills the author and his family could at last get out of the village, the diggers having finally made it through on Friday afternoon. The deep drifts that he had climbed over the previous weekend, although cut through by the diggers would be lying at the side of the road for a while yet, in fact the remains of them would still be in evidence when April arrived. Elsewhere in the south west the remains of the deepest drifts could still be seen in May.

Blizzard Memories

When the author appealed via the local press for people to contact him with their memories of the Blizzard of 78, the good people of Dorset and south Somerset responded with great enthusiasm. In the following pages are just a some of their reminiscences, in their own words.

I remember the big freeze of 1978. My wife and I had left our three children at her mother's bungalow to go out for dinner with work colleagues returning to Ferndown in the early hours.

I slept on the sofa (no not drunk or snoring but pressure of space). Waking early next morning (as you do when having consumed liberal quantities of liquid) the room seemed very light even allowing for the fact I had forgotten to close the curtains. It may have been bright but it did not mean I could see out, because the whole of the window was obscured by a 7 foot snowdrift!

The kids were soon awake, making snow caves, squealing with delight, but soon the reality of it hit me when I staggered up to Ringwood Road. I did not meet a car on my journey up the centre of the road to fetch bread for the inevitable siege. They were sold out, so Mother-in-law, being of the old school, remembered the ingredients and baked two loaves in a jiffy. I can smell them now cooling on trays in the kitchen. I can remember too their mysterious disappearance within a few minutes and the self-satisfied expression on the face of our 10 year old labrador who had taken full advantage of one of nature's miracles.

Derek M Huxley (Now retired in Blandford.)

I was living in Mappowder at the time of this bad weather and when I awoke in the morning the snow was up above the hedges, I worked for 3 days and nights non stop, moving snow with a tractor, I also took milk to King's Stag in an emergency tank to put on a milk lorry, walked to Hazelbury Bryan to get bread for the old folk from the bakery that was there, and also did a whole night at the gas works helping to check readings every hour to send back to Southampton and then go out and re adjust meters etc because they had two men who had gone 3 days on their own and could not get replacement staff until they hired a helicopter to bring two new staff in and fly the old ones out, also tried to get through to Pullham to try and get an Ambulance through to a Pregnant women at Piddletrenthide but was beaten back

Pete Dear

I recall the blizzard of 1978 quite well, and can't believe that thirty years have passed since that incredible weekend of 18th/19th February. Although the blizzard didn't compare with the length of the very cold winters of 1947 and 1963 (and I remember them pretty well too) for the sheer intensity of the storm it probably tops the lot.

I spent much of that Saturday afternoon in the garden here in Overcombe Drive. It was bitterly cold and I was fairly well wrapped up as I turned over my vegetable patch prior to sowing broad bean seeds.

An old transistor radio was on and I remember listening to a sports report from Plymouth in which soccer matches were being abandoned due to falling snow, and felt that it was quite probable that we were in for some "flurries" too.

As daylight faded, heavy snow was falling and was being whipped around in all directions by the gale force winds. Our 13 year old daughter was at a friends house for tea. It was only about a mile away, but we fully expected to hear that she was staying the night when she turned up on our doorstep with her friend's father after a tremendous struggle against the elements. After a hot drink her protector disappeared back out into the blizzard arriving back at his house after another heroic struggle. Later that evening I found that it was impossible to open our garage door and extremely difficult to close our side door because of the build up of snow.

When we awoke on the Sunday morning, we couldn't see out of any of our upstairs windows and we really thought we were entombed. Our double glazing provided good insulation however and when we went downstairs and opened the front door we realised things weren't quite as bad as we had anticipated although very severe drifting had occurred. We still couldn't open the garage door for several days and an elderly couple living in the bungalow almost opposite our house were completely cut off I recall throwing a loaf of bread to them as they stood on their parapet overlooking the road. (see Brian's picture below)

Brian Searle. Preston.

The story of Joyce and Laurie Ingham and their friends Barry and Nesta who became trapped when visiting them at Sutton Poyntz near Weymouth is told in the chapter "The blizzard strikes". Here is the rest of Joyce Ingham's story detailing events once the blizzard had stopped.

The men swept the roads as far as possible and borrowed sledges and toboggans from the children to drag up to the loop and return with much needed supplies of fresh milk and bread etc. Much excitement was caused when a helicopter had to be called to bring a pipe to a field near the water works to repair a major water leak."

Meanwhile our friends were getting to know Sutton Poyntz in much more detail than they had anticipated. and we were in danger of running out of clean underwear and warm clothes, our friends not having arrived in clothes suitable for arctic conditions. More importantly Barry carried a Yellow card because of medical conditions and had run out of medicines, so an urgent call was made to a doctor in Weymouth who arranged that the police would bring the necessary medicines to The Ship at Preston and a tractor managed to get through and brought them down to us.

It was just over a week before Barry was able to make his way to work but Nesta had to remain even longer until she was able to drive their car over top and back to Sandbanks to pick up their luggage from the hotel that they had been staying in when they visited us.

All in all quite an experience and one I will always remember, for two reasons.- First because it proved that when the chips are down people can always be relied upon to pull together. The other reason was that the adverse weather conditions had given us all the time to step back and admire the beauty of the English countryside which was brought into such sharp relief by the snow and to realise how lucky we are to live where we do.

Joyce Ingham. Weymouth

Wind sculpted snowdrifts in the countryside around Sutton Poyntz show just how beautiful the results of a blizzard can be. Pictures courtesy of Joyce Ingham.

It was about 11pm on the eve of the Great snowstorm of 1978. I was about 13 years old and unable to sleep. I looked out from under the eave of the 600 years old cottage I lived in at Wool towards the streetlamp under the Yew tree in front of the church in Church lane. Like many young boys, I always relished the prospect of snow and would quite often look out to the street light to see if was highlighting the wispy swirling character of falling snow. That night, it appeared I was in luck and I could see that snow was falling but there had been a few false dawns in the past so I wasn't about to get too excited and eventually drifted off to sleep.

I awoke the next morning to a bit of a commotion. Both my mother and my father were calling to me in very excited voices. Fearing that it was just a ruse to get a recalcitrant teenager out of bed I poked my head out from under the duvet to be met by the most incredible sight I have ever seen. Snow had indeed fallen and it had drifted right over the thatched porch and was just inches under my second storey bedroom window! My father's MK2 Daimler car had completely disappeared under the snow and the magnificent Norman church in front of the cottage appeared to be nestling in a giant hank of cotton wool. The rest of the day was spent digging our way out and joining the other amazed villagers of Wool down by the railway station.

I can remember the famous moment when the good Dr Cole our much esteemed local Doctor was whisked through the snow on a Scorpion tank to make his urgent house calls. The snow lasted about a week and we children made the best of an extra week off from school. My most endearing memory of this quite incredible event was captured in a photograph now sadly lost. It was of my mother in a short white fur coat and white hat sitting on my sledge atop a huge snowdrift that for several days completely blocked the upper half of Church Lane. I have often repeated this story to my six year old son and three year old daughter who to this day have never seen real snow in this country.

Paul Miller. Dorchester.

We lived in a semi-detached farm worker's dwelling about 100 metres up a single track gravel lane at Lambs Green Lane Corfe Mullen. I remember the event well because I had only been married a year and my first son Ben, was born on the 22nd January 1978. The lane up to the house had good hedges either side about 6 feet high and the fields sloped down to the lane. It had obviously snowed overnight and everything was very white. We had quite a large garden and the view from the garden was down over the water meadows with Wimborne Minster in the distance. I think the snow was about six inches deep in the garden. It was only later in the day when I walked out towards the lane that I realised the lane was full of snow and I mean full. It was level with the top of the hedge. The snow had obviously blown down across the field, spilled over the hedge and kept doing so until it was level with the hedge. It was three or four days before we were able to get out.

Colin Haysom.

My eighth birthday was 21st February 1978 and I remember very clearly that fantastic snow. It was half term too, so the schools were already shut. All my cards, presents and visitors were held up by the snow, which meant my birthday lasted for about a week. It was brilliant. We built snowmen, had snowball fights and my dad made us a sledge which we used to whiz down the steep hill in Parkstone which we lived at the top of.

Of course those were the days before polar fleece I think we had cagoules which were no match for the freezing conditions and I remember having soaking wet woollen gloves which we kept going in to swap for more drying on the radiators.

One day we sledged to my grandparents house in Lilliput - everything was so beautiful a true winter wonderland. I loved it so much. I love snow and I will always remember that winter. We made a massive snowball which was huge and it didn't completely disappear until April.

I really hope that my own children get to play in some of the white stuff here.

Julie Dyball. Lytchett Matravers.

We were living at Milborne St Andrew, which was cut off for several days. I have two particular memories:

We had a ten month-old baby and had run out of the only food he would really eat. Our neighbour came round and asked us if there was anything we were desperate for as he was going into Dorchester, and he then took off across country on his skis to get supplies.

The milkman couldn't get to the village, but neither could the milk tankers to collect the milk from the local farm (Hoopers in The Grove). So the only way we could get milk was to take containers and trudge through the snow to the farm, to be given milk from the enormous collecting tank where it sat and settled out. For a few days we lived on the goldest gold-top you could ever hope to see! Junket has never tasted the same since!

Felicity Maclaren

We were living in Shitterton, Bere Regis at the time.

The night before the storm my neighbour and her children came to the door and invited my sons to come and play outside, as they thought there might not be any snow the following day. This was the first snow they were old enough to remember so we dressed up warm and played outside for a time making snowmen with other kids joining in.

On the morning of the 19th we were met by a white blanket as far as the eye could see, and everything was so quiet, no traffic in the distance. My husband, in wellies, ventured outside to the shed to get a shovel and dug a path from the door to the gate, the snow being about a foot deep. We took bread out for the birds, and the boys straight away wanted to go sledging on Standbarrow hill. The favourite sledge was a fertilizer bag or a tin tray. All the village seemed to be there; kids, mums and dads, all sliding down the hill. If too many got on one bag the weight just made it go even faster, then it was a problem stopping at the bottom before crashing into the hedge.

There was no traffic moving. The previous night several cars were stuck on the cross. (We still had traffic lights before the by pass) Some had come from the Wimborne road and tried to get up Poole hill but it was impassable. People in the village provided bed and breakfast, some stayed in the Royal Oak, but a lorry carrying soldiers from Scotland to Bovington couldn't get up the hill out of the village so they slept in the Royal British Legion Club.

No milk tankers could get to the farms, so the farmers gave the milk away. We took any empty bottles and plastic containers we could find. I made rice puddings, cream cheese, clotted cream and we drank milky coffee and hot chocolate. Several people had jippy tummies as they were not used to un-pasteurised milk, but I was fine as my father had been a dairy man so I grew up with milk straight from the cow.

People could not get to work. They wandered up and down the village, as they had nothing else to do, so they stood and chatted. We met people from the other end of the parish, whom we rarely saw. Older people said it was just like the wartime spirit.

The village shops soon ran out of bread etc, and there were no papers. When one of the first cars to get to the village got through, the driver gave his paper to a lady, and she ran home with it held high, shouting, "I've got a paper!" as if it was a treasured prize.

A neighbour's daughter had been away for a while and got the train back to Wool station and then started to walk home wearing light shoes. Eventually a family member got a farmer to meet her with a tractor, and she spent several days in bed with bad feet. The doctor who lived nearby was very cross with her. The other doctor got a call out to a nearby village and he was taken to the patient in a tank from Bovington.

By the time the snow started to melt, even the children were getting fed up with it and chose to stay indoors and watch TV. The main roads were eventually freed to a single lane, but some minor roads remained closed for quite some time. Several pairs of woollen gloves had to be discarded as they had shrunk from the wet snow, there were constant puddles inside the back door from the wellies until the snow turned to muddy slush and things got back to normal.

Di Phillips. Dorchester.

The Blizzard of 1978 at Little Woolgarston near Corfe Castle.

The snow which fell very heavily overnight at that time cut off our communication with the village for over a week. It brought down overhead telephone lines and blocked Sandy Lane to the top of the hedges and filled the offshoot lane to our cottage to a depth of about twelve feet!

We had our own water supply but the electricity went off so our water pump did not work, but I was able to bale water out of the well by hand and supply our next door neighbour who had a bore but his pump was out of action too and he couldn't draw off any supply.

Being unable to use the telephone, our friends thought we were away when they rang to enquire about our welfare because the ringing tone was generated at the exchange. This was the main drawback despite no communication with the village.

A few days later when the thaw started my wife noticed that water was a dripping into our bedrooms.

When the loft was inspected I found four feet of snow was covering the first floor ceilings, actions stations were required to shovel out the snow from the upstairs window to try and prevent the bedroom ceilings collapsing. However despite this the bedroom ceilings all had to be replaced and redecorated.

The cause of the snow entering the loft space, which had never happened before since the cottage was built in the nineteenth century was that there was no weather-proofing under the tiles which were clay and mortared to the battens leaving many gaps underneath them. If you entered the loft in any windy weather it was necessary to hold your hat on due to the draught.

The council bulldozers did not clear the lane for at least seven days and the local farm had to pour a considerable quantity of milk away because the milk lorry could not enter Sandy Lane.

Colonel (Ret'd) D S Squirrell. OBE. Swanage.

A diary of the great snowstorm of 1978 at East Knighton and Winfrith.
By Noreen Guy.

15th Feb:
Heavy snowfall during the evening.

16th Feb:
No school bus. Tina made a snowman and I took a photo.

17th Feb:
No school bus.- Icy Roads. Went to Dorchester but returned early due to icy conditions.

18th Feb:

Took Stephen and Tina to Wool for Disco and on my return home skidded at East Burton roundabout and the car turned right round but I managed to get home. Couldn't get into our driveway because of a snowdrift, so parked under the garage canopy. Maurice fetched the children from Wool in the breakdown landrover, but got stuck at Newburgh Picnic area.

19th Feb:

Woke up to find deep snow .No traffic on road except snowploughs and DCC tractors at odd times - spent our time shovelling the forecourt. Shilling plot was cut off by snowdrifts . We were fortunate and never lost telephone, electricity or water like some poor people.

The view from the Rainbow garage at East Knighton looking east along the main A352 towards Wool. Picture courtesy Noreen Guy.

20th Feb:

Maurice took Mike Sullivan to Wool Station in the breakdown Landrover, (filming en route and put the film on the train for Southern ITV news). The southern part of England was the only part affected by this freak snow which seems to happen about every fifteen years. Whilst at Wool Maurice collected a crate of milk from the dairy and bread from Williams bakery and brought the supplies to the garage for those who could get to the garage on foot. Some brought their home made sledges to collect calor gas for cooking and heating. Unfortunately our supply of paraffin was low and we soon ran out. A new delivery arrived on the 23rd. A Scorpion tank from Bovington Camp brought the local doctor from Wool and went down Blacknoll Lane to attend to a patient who was ill.

21st Feb:

A foggy day. Only emergency traffic allowed on road. Maurice went to Dorchester and collected twenty one calor gas cylinders in our Luton Van. Road was single file.

Mr Carter died on the 17th February and his cremation was at Bournemouth. Crematorium on the 21st so Maurice taxied Mrs Carter, Mrs Porter and Mrs Osmond to Wool Station. The road was closed to the public at 6pm so when Maurice collected the ladies off the train at 6:50pm he had to remove the barriers across the road and replace them.

The sun came out in the afternoon so Tina and I decided to make our way to Winfrith Post Office to get some provisions we needed. Everyone was going to Winfrith,- never seen so many villagers walking - most of us have cars - it was nice to chat, but when we reached the Red Lion the road to Winfrith village was still blocked and the police were waiting for a snowplough.

However we decided to cross the fields via the Red Lion car park. Never again, with the weight of my sheepskin coat and me I began to sink.

The turning into Winfrith Newburgh from the main A352 by the Red Lion pub. The road to the village is completely blocked. Note the frozen River Win on the left of the picture. Picture courtesy Noreen Guy.

I couldn't see the hedges - Tina was light and able to skip through the snow. By the time I got level with the village hall I panicked and found my way to the high street which the snow plough had not yet reached. Eventually I got to the post office and purchased one or two items - naturally Sugar, Tea and butter were rationed, but we were grateful for what we could get and made our way back home via the High Street and Water Lane.

24th Feb:
Received first delivery of post since 18th February.

I was only eleven at the time but I can remember it quite clearly, I grew up in Sydling St Nicholas which is 9 miles from Dorchester the only access to the village was a narrow road which was easily blocked with snow.

I remember being off school for quite some time which when you're eleven is great. My parents weren't too pleased, they had the general stores and post office which by then was the only remaining shop in Sydling, food had to be rationed 2 eggs per person per week !

We also had helicopter supplies dropped in the fields which I believe my parents were responsible for.

Julia Goodwin.

Your letter brought back memories of a journey we made back home from Southampton where we were staying for the weekend with relatives. We had awoken to a considerable fall of snow (unusual for Southampton) on the Sunday morning and after listening to travel information and the weather forecast on local radio decided that we ought to cut short our visit and head home. Incidentally, our mode of transport at the time was a white (quite appropriate) Datsun Cherry!

Road conditions were not too bad until we reached Wimborne then the snow became thicker. On reaching Bere Regis we came behind a line of stationary cars and were informed by council staff that a snow plough had been through from Dorchester but as it was snowing heavily they didn't know whether it was passable.

A car from behind us went on so, undeterred and thinking safety in numbers we decided to go too, little did we know that he was only going as far as Rogers Hill (about 2 miles)! Only a single track was open and this was filling in quite quickly so the journey to Dorchester was quite hairy, all the time wondering what we would do if someone came from the opposite direction! Luckily this didn't happen although a motorcyclist, with the aid of a tractor fitted with a snow plough, did appear from the Kingston Pond area and travelled sedately in front of us into Dorchester. The town was eerily quiet, but with people walking in the road, they seemed most surprised to see our car and one person was heard to say 'where the hell did that come from?' Thankfully we didn't have to stop as although it was a front wheel drive car it would have been difficult to get going again.

We managed to get onto the Yeovil road only to find a sign by Loder's garage informing us that the road to Maiden Newton was blocked giving us fresh doubts as to whether we would make it home. For a long time our youngest son had been repeatedly asking us to stop as he needed to go to the toilet so, on reaching the Bradford Peverell turn off, this we did and consequently skidded off the road!! He's never been allowed to forget this, but with a lot of heaving and swearing we managed to get started again.

Only another quarter mile to go but the hill to our house had to be negotiated, halfway up we came to a halt but luck was still with us as a group of young lads, including our eldest son, came to our rescue. Everyone pushing and me putting Hessian sacks under the driving wheels until we eventually made it to the top and turned into our drive, much to our relief and the amazement of our next door neighbour.

Looking back we feel we were extremely fortunate to have completed that journey safely and think we were perhaps a little foolhardy to attempt it in the first place. I wonder if we were the last to get through to Dorchester on the A35 as, if I remember correctly, the county was shut by the police on the following day.

As the snow continued we were cut off for the next few days but because tankers were unable to get through to the farms, a local farmer supplied the village with milk delivered by tractor.

Ruth Smith.   Bradford Peverell

The Smith's garden and driveway upon their return to Bradford Peverell and below the view from Bradford Peverell towards the A37 just north of Dorchester. Pictures courtesy Ruth Smith.

I remember the blizzards well!

The 19th February 1978 was my 18th birthday.

My parents had arranged a huge party for me, to be held in Weymouth on Friday 17th. I had to go to college for the day and it was cold and horrible weather. I left early to help with the party, which was held at the Clifton Hotel in Weymouth

As the evening wore on I got more and more messages from friends in the villages saying that they couldn't make it in because of the snow - but it wasn't snowing were I was.

Over the weekend it began to snow in earnest. My sisters boyfriend, a motorbike rider had been given permission to stay at our house overnight sleeping on the couch. The following day the snow got even heavier and deeper and he kept saying he would leave soon, but wanted to stay a bit longer. Of course it became clear that he wouldn't be able to ride home at all.

On my birthday itself, Sunday 19th, the snow was very deep outside. It looked great but had taken the edge off my party celebrations and on the Monday my sister's boyfriend eventually got a lift home from his dad who was fed up at having to drive around in the snow.

Funny thing though. The DJ at my party, well two years later I met him at work and he asked me out. We got married on 25th April 1981 and there was a blizzard that day as well.

Jenny Vincent (nee Greatrex)

_____

We lived in a flat above a shop in Cheap street in Sherborne and my daughter had a friend to stay for the weekend but when we got cut off she kept crying for her mother. My late husband said he couldn't stick her crying all the time and that we would walk her back to Bradford Abbas where she lived. We only had one pair of wellies for her to wear and my daughter was upset because she couldn't come.

We set off along Bradford road, had to get into a field was the snow as too deep on the road and I got stuck, my husband had to pull me out, from then on we were in and out of the fields and the road. We eventually arrived at the girls home, left her and started straight back on our journey home. We knew we couldn't go back the same way that we had come because we would have had to climb down from the fields on to the road and wouldn't have been able to get back up because of the deep drifts.

We made our way to the Bradford hollow. Cars had got stuck under the snow all the way down. We managed to get onto the dual carriageway (A30) . In some places there was no snow at all, in others it was very deep. It was now quite dark and a blizzard started up and I really thought I was going to die. I told my husband to leave me, but he just caught hold of my hand and made me keep going. We arrived back home at 8:45pm, having left Sherborne at 1:pm. My son had to pull my wellies off as they were packed tight with snow, my poor husband only had ankle boots on. His words to my daughter upon our return were "Don't you ever invite friends to stay again!"

B. Barter. Sherborne

Conditions just over the border in south Somerset were just as bad as they were in Dorset as the following letters indicate.

I was teaching at Wadham School in Crewkerne in 1978 when the blizzard struck. I was then living in Merriott just to the north of

Crewkerne and following the storm my wife and I took our daughters on a walk into Crewkerne and subsequently on to Wadham School.

The village was cut off for three days and one of my main memories was that of local farmers meeting in the centre of the village, just outside my house, to arrange to put all of their livestock into one field to facilitate feeding. During the three days in which no vehicles came into the village a local farmer provided us with free unpasteurised milk. That which he didn't give away was just being thrown away.

Mike Edwards. Yeovil

Mike Edwards took this picture of his wife and daughters as they walked along the road from Merriott to Crewkerne. As can be seen the drift completely blocked the road. Picture courtesy Mike Edwards.

Deep drifts in Somerset on the main A359 road at Three Ashes between Galhampton and North Cadbury and below the road between Three Ashes and North Cadbury. Pictures courtesy Mr P. Brewin.

At that time, Feb 1978. I was working as a staff nurse on the children's ward at Yeovil District Hospital. When the blizzard came on the evening of 18th February various children who would have been discharged were unable to get home. We had numbers of parents 'stuck' with them. By the next day we were already at bursting point and by Monday even worse as several emergency admissions came in by helicopter from Frome and Street as well as a sick baby from North Cadbury. Initially the helicopter landed on the roundabout, a very skilled task, but as some roads access became cleared they were using Mudford recreation grounds as a landing pad.

I was able to walk to the hospital and back and did several extra duties to fill in for staff who couldn't get in from outlying areas. It was a magical time really especially walking up the Ilchester Road at 9pm with complete quiet a nearly full moon and deep unblemished snow all around.

However it did cause problems for the hospital. Staff who had been marooned there slept wherever a bed could be found and day staff swapped with night staff. The parents who couldn't get home soon ran out of clothes and I remember one dad being most grateful when I lent him a couple of pairs of my husbands pants!

There was a great spirit of camaraderie at the hospital really, I quite enjoyed the whole experience. By Wednesday 22nd there was a single track cleared along Combe St. Lane we could then begin to move children out and accept admissions by more normal routes.

Prim Lee. Yeovil.

At the time of the 1978 blizzard I had been a consultant surgeon at Yeovil for two years. Fortunately I lived within ten minutes walking time of the hospital. The snow and ice came very quickly and it prevented staff from coming to work and others from going home. The whole regime of the health care system had to be changed to accommodate the crisis. Nurses who could not get home were asked to work double shifts and then accommodated in the nursing school classrooms with mattresses and blankets.

The junior resident doctors were able to attend as they lived across the road from the hospital. The senior staff numbers were decimated because most of them served more than one hospital and lived in the villages. It was decided to stop all routine surgery, clinics and outpatients. Supplies including blood products could not be brought to the hospital and the stored on site, supplies were very limited. The main blood bank was in Bristol, some 45 miles away over the Mendips.

The medical consultant physicians lived out in the surrounding villages and could not get to the hospital and it was decided that all the non surgical wards would be under the care of the senior anaesthetist who, like me, lived within walking distance of the hospital. I was able to look after the non orthopaedic surgical patients. One of my colleagues lived in Beaminster and was unable to come in for several days.

Patients who were due to discharged had to stay in the wards as ambulances could not navigate the roads. Eventually the Royal Navy helicopters were called in to pick up women in labour and other emergencies from the countryside and were able to land them on the roundabout on the A30 next to the hospital. A pregnant woman was airlifted in from Ilchester in this way.

The icy and slippery snow produced the usual crop of fractured bones and these had the attention of an orthopaedic surgeon who managed to get in from his home in a land rover. A gentleman of the road was brought in by the police with frostbite in his toes. Each year he usually lost one toe but this time all the remaining toes were amputated!

My children were able to ice skate on the roads and we collected milk from the Hendford Dairy by sledge. There was no way milk could be delivered safely any other way.

It took a long time for the roads to be made safe and as the various villages were liberated the staff numbers increased. People in Odcombe had to wait over a week before relief came. They were well and truly snowed in!

David Griffiths

The story of Brendon and Lin

The following story was sent to the author by Brendon Owen of Montacute in south Somerset. It reads like a boys own adventure.

In February 1978 my wife and I were living in the village of Montacute in South Somerset (as we still do). The 18th was a Saturday and we woke to find there had been reasonable fall of snow in the night. The morning was dry and bright. I took my wife for a toboggan run on the hill behind our house.

In the early afternoon we drove to Westbury in Wiltshire for a friend's birthday party. I should have known that something was amiss when I looked at the 5pm football results on the T.V. I commented that it was unusual to see a home game for Plymouth Argyle to be abandoned because of heavy snow. I thought no more about it.

Following the party we drove with our friends to a pub in Nunney to finish off the evening, At closing time we said our goodbyes and set off on our separate journeys, they back to Westbury, Lin and I back to Montacute. It was snowing quite heavily as we walked through the car park and it was necessary to clear the windscreen of the fresh fall but nothing out of the ordinary.

As we drove west, the snow became heavier and heavier and the roads more and more difficult. Eventually we reached a road where a 'road closed' sign had been erected and we were forced to take a smaller road which we were unfamiliar with. I was driving a Renault 5 and the windscreen wipers even on full speed were finding it impossible to sweep away the amount of snow that was falling. As we drove, the car began to slip and slide all over the place and everything outside became just one white sheet. I could not tell if I was going forwards, backwards or sideways! Several times I must have glanced off the tall hedgerows because we could hear the scraping sounds. I was driving as carefully as I could but the situation was becoming hopeless.

Lin was not unnaturally afraid and I was not feeling at all good about the position either. We saw no living soul but pushed on . We could not tell if there were any houses about as we just could not see outside. This huge white sheet had been thrown over us and our world was just the interior of the car.

We hadn't the faintest idea where we were but we knew we could not possibly go much further. We started up an incline and the car was out of control. The steering wheel was useless and we just slid backwards. I managed to hold the vehicle on the handbrake and we sat and looked at each other. As we did so the snow was piling up around the car and we realised that if we didn't get out then, we may not be getting out at all! I had to force the door on the drivers side because a drift was forming against the door. I got Lin out of her side and retrieved a spade from the boot. Fortunately we were both wearing thick dufflecoats with hoods which we immediately put up.

In seconds we had both turned white as we stood looking at our geographical position. We were in country lane with high hedges on either side and fields stretching away. Through the blizzard we could see a faint light and we made our way towards it. There was an isolated house on the hill and I knocked at the door. A bedroom window opened and a man called down to us. I didn't quite know what to say to him. So I asked him where the nearest village was. He pointed back down the hill and said it was called Batcombe. We thanked him and headed in the direction he gave. We hung on to each other because not only was it snowing like the devil but the wind was screaming and howling as well. We struggled down the hill and saw more lights at the bottom. A large house loomed up and we waded down the driveway and beat on the door We must have looked like two snowmen stood at the door when it opened. I had a full beard at that time and the snow in the freezing conditions had turned to ice and hung from me like Scott of the Antarctic.

We thought if we could get to the village rectory we might be given some assistance there and so we asked at this very posh house for the vicar. After very brief instructions the door banged loudly in our faces. We staggered off back down the drive and into the road which by now was totally devoid of any features. The snow was a foot or two deep and we had great difficulty making any headway.

We sheltered by a big stone wall and weighed up our options I didn't think there was much prospect of finding the rectory as we could only see a couple of feet in front of our eyes and we had reached some sort of cross roads. We then saw a terrace of small cottages at an angle to the road and pushed on until we got to a door. A man answered and almost before I had a chance to speak he pulled both Lin and I into his kitchen. He told us there was no way we were going to stay out there a minute longer and that he and his family would help us.

They were a lovely family (for my shame, I cannot recall their name after all this time) and were the salt of the earth. Generous country folk who would share their last bit of food with you. They lived in two terraced cottages that had been made into one and the other cottage in the terrace was lived in by one of their sons. He was away for the weekend and it was agreed that we should spend the night there. After a hot drink we shuffled back out into the blizzard which was raging as fiercely as ever and entered this little cottage. The disadvantage of the son being away was that the heating had been turned off and the place was like an ice cavern. We occupied his double bed keeping all our clothes on other than our now soaked duffle coats. We clung to each other for warmth but I'm sure I must have kept Lin awake with the noise of my chattering teeth! The wind moaned and screeched and the snow beat at the window all night but by daylight, whatever time that was, it seemed to have subsided.

We opened the door of the cottage and a wall of snow faced us. We pushed our way through and joined our 'family' in their wonderfully warm kitchen. Bacon was sizzling in the pan and it never smelt so good! They told us they had been listening to the radio and the situation across the southwest was incredible. Everywhere was cut off from everywhere else and the services were struggling to get going. Our host had a smallholding and was worried about his sheep. He was also the volunteer snowplough driver for the village. Batcombe, being in the Mendip hills, was quite accustomed to snow but he had been unable to get near the garage that the plough was housed in.

We spent part of the morning digging out the path along the cottages down to the road. I then got it into my head that I should go and check on my car and left Lin with the family and started the difficult manoeuvre of getting back up the hill. The snow was so deep that I had to climb up on top of the hedgerows and walk along the top if them, they were so packed with snow that they held my weight. The road had completely gone and only the twigs on the tops of the hedges were visible. I spied the house that we had originally called at the night before but could see no sign of my car. Eventually I saw the tip of the aerial which was on the roof poking a couple of inches out of the snow.

The chap who had called down from his window saw me and invited me in for a coffee, He apologised for not realising the seriousness of the situation the night before and said he would have taken us in had he known. He offered to hold my car keys for me and if the opportunity arose he would try and move my car onto his property before the snowplough came barging it's way up the lane (We heard some weeks later that a mini that was trapped in the snow nearby had been damaged by the plough).

Back at the cottage we settled in for our second night. The wife brought out the photo albums and regaled us with stories of the winter of 1962/63

162

when Batcombe was cut off from the world for weeks on end and they had to mark a big cross in the field for the helicopter to drop provisions for them.

During the day I had made phone calls to our next door neighbours in Montacute to explain and ask them to look after our cat, who was stuck in the house unable to get through the cat flap because of the snow. We also phoned our friends in Westbury only to be told that the snow wasn't much of a problem there. They promised to come and rescue us as soon as conditions improved.

We ate well, we were warm, we were very well looked after by our family and their two lurcher dogs who pounced on any loose scraps of food as if their lives depended upon it. We listened to the radio reports, hundreds of roads blocked, people trapped, cars abandoned. We were in for the duration.

On the Monday (20th) Lin and I ventured out and made it to the village shop where we bought a couple of toothbrushes and as we returned we passed the most enormous snowdrift I have ever seen. We had to crane our necks to see the top of it, without exaggeration it must have been Twenty feet high if it was inch. It was breathtakingly beautiful. Sculptured by the wind it stood like a huge sail on a yacht. If only I had had my camera with me.

Several days passed and we were all preparing to sit down to a huge dish of shepherds pie when there was a knock at the door. Our friends from Westbury had driven as far as they were able and then made their way across the fields to find us. We couldn't impose on our family any longer and took our grateful leave of them without tasting that delicious looking shepherds pie! We swapped addresses and promised to keep in touch.

With our two friends, we decided to go to the local pub and eat something before setting off on the long journey on foot. We ordered a plate full of ham sandwiches and were informed that we were very lucky as it was the last of the bread and ham that they had. We sat down and had a beer and looked up to see the waitress coming across the flag stone floor with heaped ham sandwiches. What we didn't see was the pub's dog get under her feet and trip her up. The plates of sandwiches spilled from her hands and scattered across the floor. The dog was upon them before we could move and so we had a mars bar each and left the pub

Back in Westbury you would wonder what all the fuss had been about. Very little snow remained and we thought we would soon be going home. We of course were without our car and looked to the train time table to return to Yeovil. There were of course no trains running and so in Westbury we had to stay.

We caught the first train that ran back to Yeovil and then walked the five miles or so to Montacute still tramping through deep snow.

A week later a friend drove me back to Batcombe and I was reunited with my car. I would have never recognized the area, without the snow it looked completely different. I called in to see our 'family' and was able to give them the news that Lin had been confirmed pregnant with our first child. She hadn't thought it wise to alert me to the possibility whilst we were tramping through the snow!

A little parcel of hand knitted baby clothes came eight months later from the good people of Batcombe who will always hold a place in our hearts.

Severe drifting seen here in Aller Lane at Ansty. Pictures courtesy of Anne and Alan Stephens.

Shaftesbury the highest town in Dorset suffered along with the rest of the county during the blizzard of 78. Pictures courtesy of Mrs Hobby (top) and Dave Davis.

Going nowhere, vehicles trapped in the drifts at Mayford Road in the Bourne Valley district on the Poole/Bournemouth boundary Picture courtesy Chris and Lyn Pullen.

Why did it happen and could it happen again?

In its most basic form the great blizzard of February 1978 was simply a clash between very cold air originating from Russia and eastern Europe and mild moist air from the Atlantic, but of course there is far more to it than just that. After all, cold and mild air masses clash numerous times each year across southern England, so what was different about February 1978?

We can learn quite a lot by looking at the great winters of modern history, because in many ways the cold spell and blizzards of February 1978 were a microcosm of these; A classic hard winter scenario squeezed into two and a bit weeks as it were.

The two harshest winters of the twentieth century were those of 1947 and 1963 with 1947 being by far the snowiest and 1963 being very much the coldest. Yet despite both of them being extremely harsh, they were quite different in character. The winter of 1947 didn't really get going until the final week of January 1947 while the winter of 1963 got under way in during Christmas 1962.

After its relatively late start the winter of 1947 was marked out by very cold but cloudy weather and frequent heavy snowfalls, indeed snow fell somewhere in Britain everyday between the 22nd January and the 17th March in 1947. The winter of 1963 after its initial snowfalls and blizzards in late December 1962, saw bitterly cold but often sunny weather with just two further major blizzards.

The thread that runs through both of these long harsh winters is that the weather was being controlled by large areas of high pressure to our north and east, allowing very cold air from Russia and Scandinavia to flood across Britain. In the great majority of our winters the weather is controlled by low pressure in the Atlantic keeping the Britain in mainly mild and often moist air. Hence our average winters especially in the south are generally cloudy, mild and damp affairs.

It has been mentioned already that mild air and cold air masses commonly clash over southern England. However in the vast majority of cases the mild air wins hands down sweeping any cold and frosty weather aside as it floods in from the southwest.

In the winters of 1947 and 1963 the high pressure steadfastly anchored to our north and east ensured that it was the bitterly cold air that held sway. Any mild moist air trying to move across Britain had to fight for every inch of ground and was repeatedly slowed down and then repulsed. The slow moving battle zones where the mild moist air and the bitterly cold air met and slugged it out were where the great snowstorms of those winters occurred.

The question that could be asked of the author at this point is why not write a book about the great snowstorms of 1947 and 1963? The answer is simple. The snowstorms of those great winters were just features of the bitterly cold regimes that held sway for weeks on end and therefore were not that unexpected. The two week cold spell and phenomenal blizzard of February 1978 occurred in the mildest part of mainland Britain, in an otherwise unremarkable winter, and that is what makes it (for the author at least) a far more interesting subject.

The situation that built up between the 8th and 18th February 1978 was in retrospect, setting up the classic conditions for a heavy snowfall event to make maximum impact. Bitterly cold days followed by severe night frosts cooled the ground dramatically while immediately prior to the blizzard the bitter south-easterly gale ensured that the ground was blown dry of moisture, creating conditions that any falling snowflake would relish.

By the time the first snowfall arrived on the night of the 15th February everything was in place for a classic snowfall set up. The high pressure area that had been feeding bitterly cold air across the south had been in - situ for a week and half, and the first of two small areas of moisture laden low pressure was forced to slide south eastwards across the west country keeping Dorset in the bitterly cold air whilst feeding in moisture which fell as snow. The snowfall event on the night of the 16th was practically a carbon copy of that on the 15th. Both of these low pressure systems were relatively small discrete bodies of air that were moving fairly fast so once they had passed through (a period of a few hours) the snowfall ceased.

The main blizzard on the 18th/19th was caused by a somewhat different set up. Early on Saturday 18th the high pressure to the east was still feeding bitterly cold air into Britain but a weather front separating the bitter arctic air from the much milder air further west stretched all the way from the southern tip of Greenland down through the far south-west of Ireland across the Scilly Isles, through the Brest peninsular and down into southern France. This weather front represented the battle zone between the milder air trying to push into the southwest and the cold air over Britain. Yet again just as on the 15th and 16th the mild air was forced to rise up over the bitterly cold air because the high pressure would not give way and once again the moisture it released fell as snow.

The problem this time though was that as the weather front moved into the south-west it was forced to slow down by the stubborn colder air and it eventually ground to a halt with its leading edge running along a line from the Isle of Wight north-westwards to Cardigan Bay. In so doing the whole snow making process that was taking place in the skies above Dorset, Devon and Somerset also ground to a halt and just continued to dump snow over large parts of those counties for between twenty and thirty hours.

Similar battle zones to this also occurred in 1947 and 1963 and also in the great Victorian blizzards of Jan 1881 and March 1891. Indeed in Dorset one would have to go back to the blizzard of January 1881 to find more severe conditions than those that occurred in February 1978. The snows of 1947 and 1963 may have stayed on the ground for far longer and therefore created a longer lasting problem, but for the severity of the drifting and depth of the overall fall especially over the lower ground. The Blizzard of February 18th/19th 1978 was without parallel in the twentieth century across the counties of Devon and Dorset.

Accurate snow depth measurements are always difficult to assess in severe blizzard conditions but evidence from weather enthusiasts along with measurements taken at various weather stations across the south west suggest that a 10-12 inch fall was common place on the lower ground. On higher ground however that figure rises dramatically to between 15 and 18 inches. However some level depths well in excess of this were also reported at the time

To give some insight into this we need to travel across Dorset's western border into Devon and do a comparison. During the Siberian winter of 1963, the snow depth at Princetown on Dartmoor stood at 18 inches on the 1st January. By the 31st of January 1963 this had increased to 20 inches. And following another severe blizzard on the 6th February the overall depth had risen to 22 inches. A phenomenal depth of snow that had built up during six weeks of bitter cold and numerous snowfalls.

Yet in February 1978 after just two weeks of cold weather, two average snowfalls and one major blizzard the snow depth at Princetown on the 19th February was a staggering 24 inches! Further north on the highest parts of Exmoor a maximum recorded level depth of 36 inches was reported.

According to detailed research by Britain's foremost authority on historic snowfalls, Dr Richard Wild of WeatherNet Ltd, the 36 inch snow depth on Exmoor confirms the Blizzard of 78 as the third deepest snowfall event to occur in Britain in the last 150 years. (Please see references below)

Without doubt the most outstanding feature of the blizzard of 78 was the extremely severe drifting. Several winters in the period between 1977 and 1987 produced snowfall with substantial drifting in Dorset but they rarely produced drifting in excess of 3- 5 feet.

Such drifting in the blizzard of 78 would have been considered rather puny. Drifting within the range 6 to 10 feet was common place with much of the drifting in the rural areas coming into the 10 to 20 feet bracket. The most exposed and geographically susceptible locations saw drifting 20 to 30 feet deep. Some of the very deepest drifts that built up against farm buildings were reported to be around 40 feet deep or more.

Accounts were also given of stream valleys and ravines filling up with snow, with at least one report of a 60 feet deep ravine on Exmoor being "filled to the brim". Unfortunately at the time of writing no photographic confirmation has come to light.

References

Wild, R. (2005) *A spatial and temporal analysis of heavy snowfalls across Great Britain between the years 1861-1999.* Unpublished PhD Thesis, University of Derby, 344 pp
Wild, R. (2007) A review of heavy snowfalls/blizzards/snowstorms greater than 13cm in Great Britain between 1861-1996: Part 7: 1976-1979. *The International Journal of Meteorology*, **32**, pp. 325-334
Wild, R. (1996) Frequency of blizzards and heavy snowfalls greater than 15 centimetres across Great Britain 1861-1995. *Journal of Meteorology*, **21**, 217
Wild, R.; O'Hare, G. and Wilby, R. (1996) A historical record of blizzards/major snow events in the British Isles, 1880-1989. *Weather*, **51**, 82-91
Wild, R.; O'Hare, G. and Wilby, R. (2000) An analysis of heavy snowfalls/blizzards/snowstorms and snowfalls greater than 13cm across Great Britain between 1861 and 1996. *Journal of Meteorology*, **25**, 41-49

Could it happen again?

It would be very easy to think that in these times where global warming is the watchword and all the talk is of an ongoing rise in temperatures, that a cold spell and blizzards like that of February 1978 simply couldn't happen any more.

That would be a rather short sighted way of looking at the situation. We have already seen that great winters like 1947 and 1963 are extremely rare. However, as the blizzard of 78 proved you don't need to have a severe winter in order to endure severe blizzard conditions. It should be remembered that the winter of 1978 was not cold enough overall to rate a place on the list of the top twenty coldest winters of the twentieth century.

All that would be required for a repeat of the blizzard of 78 is a very similar pressure set up to that which occurred at that time. Even allowing for the undoubted warming that has occurred during the last thirty years or so.

One should not forget that even allowing for our current period of warming the winter of 2006 was one of the coldest and snowiest for many years across much of Europe and western Russia. On several occasions during that winter the boundary between the moderately cold conditions over Britain and the bitter conditions over Europe was only 100 miles or so to our east. On several other occasions in the last ten years Britain has escaped harsh winter weather by the skin of its teeth as bitter conditions have roared out of the arctic and down across the North Sea into Scandinavia and Europe. It would be foolish to think that our luck can hold out indefinitely in this regard.

An argument could also be made that the snow might be even heavier if exactly the same pressure pattern were to occur again today, because the relative warming that has occurred in recent times would mean that the mild air that would be forced to rise over the cold block and release its moisture would be warmer than it was back in 1978 and therefore be able to hold even more moisture thus creating even more snow.

Some might argue that the seas around us have warmed somewhat since 1978 and therefore should the same situation arise again then the bitterly cold air coming from eastern Europe would be significantly warmed as it crossed the north sea. However this would be missing the point entirely because during the blizzard of 78 the cold air that affected southern England arrived from the southeast, taking the shortest sea route possible across the English Channel. This combined with the fact that it was moving extremely fast meant that any warming effect by the sea was almost non existent.

Should we be visited by conditions like February 1978 again. How would we cope? Back in the seventies most public utilities employed far more people than they do now. Thirty years on, many of these bodies have been trimmed to the bone by reorganisation or privatisation. The question that arises is do any of the public bodies still have the manpower to deal with such a crisis. In Dorset it is now over twenty years since there has been a notably deep countywide snowfall so it's not as if we have had the chance to practice and keep our hand in.

One thing that has undoubtedly improved since 1978 is the standard of weather forecasting and hopefully any future extreme snowstorm like the blizzard of 78 would be picked up on somewhat earlier, giving the powers that be more time to prepare. The forecasting may well have improved but whenever the next notably deep snowfall occurs in Dorset; and occur it will. It will be interesting to see if all of our technological advances during the last 30 years have left us any better at coping with a drop of the white stuff.

A mother and child dwarfed by the drifting snow at Ansty during the blizzard of 78. Could it happen again? The answer is yes. It's just a matter of when. Picture courtesy of Anne and Alan Stephens.

Further Reading and information.

Magasines and Journals.

The International journal of Meteorology.
www.ijmet.org

Weather: Published by the Royal Meteorolgical Society
www rjmets.org

Weathereye: Published by Frosted Earth.
Ian@frostedearth.com. Or 01737 554869.

Forecasts and historical weather information.

WeatherNet Ltd.
WeatherNet is a professional, non-government provider of on line weather applications, data sets, reports, consultancy and advice.

Telephone:
General enquiries: 01202 293868
Fax 01202-314064
e-mail: info@weathernet.co.uk

Postal Address:
WeatherNet Ltd
Kingsland House
21 Hinton Road
Bournemouth
Dorset BH1 2DE

Websites
www.theweatheroutlook.com
www.netweather.tv

About the Author

Mark's lifelong interest in our weather was fired in his childhood by stories told to him by his great grandmother of the legendary Victorian blizzards of 1881 and 1891.

Born in Bournemouth in 1960, he was educated at Bournemouth School for Boys before leaving in 1976 to become a Thatcher. A craft that has given him ample time to study the skies of Dorset. An injury induced break from thatching saw him further his meteorological interest working for WeatherNet Ltd before returning to the trade in 2005.

In 1997 he co-authored The Dorset Weather Book with Ian Currie and has since then written a weekly weather column for the (Newsquest) Echo newspaper series as well as supply articles for the Dorset, and Dorset Life magazines. Mark has given over 300 talks about various aspects of weather as well a having appeared in various programmes about weather on the BBC, Meridian TV and Channel Four. Mark is married to Julie, a Chiropodist, and they live in rural south Dorset where they share their cottage with an ageing and slightly mad cat.